IMPACT
CALIFORNIA
SOCIAL STUDIES

INQUIRY JOURNAL

WORLD
HISTORY & GEOGRAPHY

MEDIEVAL & EARLY MODERN TIMES

Jackson J. Spielvogel, Ph.D.

Mc
Graw
Hill
Education

Cover credits: (t to b, l to r)Getty Images/Will Selarep; (2)© Nigel Spooner / Alamy; (3)Yuri Yavnik/Shutterstock ; (4)© Ian Nellist / Alamy; (5) Image courtesy National Gallery of Art

mheducation.com/prek-12

Send all queries to:
McGraw-Hill Education
8787 Orion Place
Columbus, OH 43240

ISBN: 978-0-07-906350-2
MHID: 0-07-906350-0

Printed in the United States of America.

4 5 6 7 8 9 QSX 23 22 21 20 19 18

Table of Contents

Dear Student,

Most of us are curious, and we have questions about many things. We have the more personal questions, such as, "Will my favorite book be made into a movie?" or "Why does my former best friend not want to hang out with me anymore?" to questions of a larger nature about the world around us. These might include questions such as: "What does being treated like an adult mean?" "Why can't people share?" "Why do we have to go to war?" "How do I understand what I see or read about in history or online or in the news?" and "Why is the peace process so difficult?"

Asking good questions helps us take charge of our own learning. Learning to ask good questions is a process, as "yes" and "no" types of questions do not get us very far in discovering why events happened or why people feel as they do. Once we master this process, however, we become better thinkers and researchers and can find out more about subjects that interest us. Asking good questions is also important if we want to understand and affect the world around us.

In this book, as in other parts of this program, there will be "Essential Questions" that you will research. These types of questions concern all people – those who have lived, those who are living now, and those who will live in the future. Examples of these questions include: "How do new ideas change the way people live?" "What makes a culture unique?" "What characteristics make a good leader?" and "Why does conflict develop?" You will choose some of your own supporting questions to help you answer the Essential Question.

As you move through the study of history, you will be reading primary and secondary sources about a specific time period. Primary sources—whether they are diaries, poetry, letters, or artwork—were created by people who saw or experienced the event they are describing. Secondary sources—whether they are biographies, history books, or your student text—are created after an event by people who were not part of the original event.

Once you have completed the readings and the text notes, there is a "Report Your Findings" project in which you answer the Essential Question. You will work on some parts of the project by yourself, and you will work on other parts of the project with your classmates. You will be given many opportunities to take informed action. This means that you will use what you have learned and apply it to a current issue in a way that interests you. You will share this information with other students or with people outside of the classroom.

Rome and the Rise of Christianity

ESSENTIAL QUESTION
What are the characteristics of a leader?

Think about how this question might relate to Rome and the rise of Christianity. What kind of leaders emerged that influenced society? How did different leadership styles influence society and the rise of different empires and religions?

TALK ABOUT IT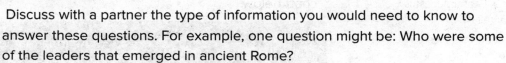

Discuss with a partner the type of information you would need to know to answer these questions. For example, one question might be: Who were some of the leaders that emerged in ancient Rome?

MY RESEARCH QUESTIONS

Supporting Question 1:

_____

_____

Supporting Question 2:

_____

_____

Supporting Question 3:

_____

_____

ESSENTIAL QUESTION

What are the characteristics of a leader?

As you gather evidence to answer the Essential Question, think about:

- the characteristics of Roman leaders such as Caesar Augustus and Marcus Aurelius.
- how these leaders influenced Roman culture.

My Notes

_____

_____

_____

_____

_____

_____

_____

_____

_____

_____

Rome's Decline

DIRECTIONS: Search for evidence in Chapter 1, Lesson 1 to help you answer the following questions.

1 **IDENTIFYING** What led to the political confusion that took place after the Pax Romana?

_____

_____

_____

_____

2 **HISTORY** Fill in the missing information on Roman society in the chart below.

Role in Rome's Society	Actions that led to Rome's Decline
	Stopped paying taxes
Government officials	
	Fought each other to replace the emperor
Emperors	

3 **SUMMARIZING** In what ways did Diocletian try to restore order to Rome?

_____

_____

_____

_____

4A **DESCRIBING** Why did Germanic tribes invade Rome?

_____

_____

_____

_____

_____

4B **ANALYZING** How did these invasions contribute to the fall of the Roman Empire?

_____

_____

_____

_____

_____

5 CIVICS Fill in the graphic organizer below with two to three details about each of the following key players in the Roman Empire.

Diocletian	Constantine	Alaric
• _____	• _____	• _____
• _____	• _____	• _____
• _____	• _____	

ESSENTIAL QUESTION

What are the characteristics of a leader?

VOCABULARY

consular: annually elected chief magistrate

ovation: a ceremony attending the entering of Rome

curule: a high-ranking dignitary

imperator: a commander-in-chief or emperor

laurels: a crown awarded as an honor

legates: official emissaries

auspices: kindly patronage and guidance

tribunician: resembling a Roman tribune or his office

The Ancyra Inscription

DIRECTIONS: Read the following excerpt and answer the accompanying questions.

EXPLORE THE CONTEXT: Caesar Augustus was the founder of the Roman Principate and considered the first Roman emperor, controlling the empire from 27 B.C.E. until his death in 14 C.E. Written by Caesar Augustus about his own reign, the Ancyra Inscription was carved on a temple shortly after Augustus's death.

PRIMARY SOURCE: HISTORICAL ACCOUNT

66 When I was nineteen I collected an army on my own account and at my own expense, by the help of which I restored the republic to liberty, . . . for which services the Senate, in complimentary decrees, added my name to the roll of their House. . . , giving me at the same time consular precedence [priority] in voting; and gave me imperium [supreme civil and military power]. It ordered me as propraetor [highest judicial authority] "to see along with the consuls that the republic suffered no damage." . . . I had to undertake wars by land and sea, civil and foreign, all over the world, and when victorious I spared all citizens who asked for pardon. Those foreign nations, who could safely be pardoned, I preferred to preserve rather than exterminate. . . . I twice celebrated an ovation, three times curule triumphs, and was twenty-one times greeted as imperator. Though the Senate afterwards voted me several triumphs I declined them. I frequently also deposited laurels in the Capitol after performing the vows which I had taken in each war. For successful operations performed by myself or by my legates under my auspices by land and sea, the Senate fifty-three times decreed a supplication [prayer] to the immortal gods. . . . I had been consul thirteen times at the writing of this, and am in the course of the thirty-seventh year of my tribunician power [13–14 C.E.]. 99

—from *Augustus: The Life and Times of the Founder of the Roman Empire*

1 **INFERRING** How many times does Caesar Augustus use the word "I" in this passage? What does this tell you about his character?

_____

_____

_____

_____

_____

2 **ANALYZING** What do you think Caesar Augustus's purpose is in writing this passage?

_____

_____

_____

_____

_____

3 HISTORY What are some of Caesar Augustus's accomplishments, according to the excerpt? What evidence can you cite from the excerpt?

_____

_____

_____

_____

4 **CONNECT TO TODAY** What similar achievements would a modern-day leader possibly list?

_____

_____

_____

_____

ESSENTIAL QUESTION

What are the characteristics of a leader?

VOCABULARY

vilest: most evil

coerce: force

forsooth: in truth, implies contempt or doubt

embellished: decorated

The Annals of Tacitus

DIRECTIONS: Read the following excerpt about the funeral of Roman Emperor Augustus and answer the accompanying questions.

EXPLORE THE CONTEXT: Publius Cornelius Tacitus was a senator and a historian of the Roman Empire. In his two major works of writing, the *Annals* and the *Histories*, he examined the reigns of several Roman emperors. He is considered to be one of the greatest Roman historians and is known for his serious examinations of politics.

PRIMARY SOURCE: BOOK

" On the day of the funeral soldiers stood round as a guard, amid much ridicule [scorn] from those who had either themselves witnessed or who had heard from their parents of the famous day when slavery was still something fresh, and freedom had been resought [attempted again] in vain [hopelessly], when the slaying [killing] of [Julius] Caesar, the Dictator, seemed to some the vilest, to others, the most glorious of deeds. "Now," they said, "an aged sovereign [ruler], whose power had lasted long, who had provided his heirs with abundant means to coerce the State, requires forsooth the defence of soldiers that his burial may be undisturbed." . . .

. . . the State had been organized under the name neither of a kingdom nor a dictatorship, but under that of a prince. The ocean and remote rivers were the boundaries of the empire; the legions, provinces, fleets, all things were linked together; there was law for the citizens; there was respect shown to the allies. The capital had been embellished on a grand scale; only in a few instances had he resorted to force, simply to secure general tranquility [peace]. . . . No doubt, there was peace after all this, but it was a peace stained with blood. . . "

— Tacitus, *Annals*, Book 1, 109 C.E.

1 HISTORY What accomplishments did others praise in Caesar Augustus that he also wrote about himself in the previous source?

_____

_____

_____

_____

2 CONTRASTING How does this excerpt about the funeral of Caesar Augustus differ from the text he wrote about himself in the previous source? Cite examples from the texts.

_____

_____

_____

_____

_____

_____

3 DISTINGUISHING FACT FROM OPINION Is this passage a factual account, or is it mostly opinion? Explain your answer.

_____

_____

_____

_____

_____

4 MAKE CONNECTIONS In the excerpt, Augustus is described as using force rarely and only when needed to achieve peace. What other leaders or historical events might fit this description?

_____

_____

_____

ESSENTIAL QUESTION

What are the characteristics of a leader?

As you gather evidence to answer the Essential Question, think about:

- the characteristics of Byzantine leaders. such as Justinian and Constantine.
- how these leaders influenced Byzantine culture.

My Notes

_____

_____

_____

_____

_____

_____

_____

_____

_____

_____

The Byzantine Empire

DIRECTIONS: Search for evidence in Chapter 1, Lesson 2 to help you answer the following questions.

1 GEOGRAPHY List two of the major reasons that Constantinople thrived as the capital of the Byzantine Empire.

_____

_____

_____

_____

2A **EXPLAINING CAUSES** Why do you think Latin culture and language were displaced by Greek culture and language in the Byzantine Empire?

_____

_____

_____

_____

2B **MAKE CONNECTIONS** How do cultures influence one another? Give at least one example from American life today to support your explanation.

_____

_____

_____

_____

_____

3 HISTORY   How did Theodora influence Justinian?

_____

_____

_____

_____

_____

4 **INTEGRATING INFORMATION** What can you infer about Byzantine culture from the building of the Hagia Sophia?

_____

_____

_____

_____

5 **ANALYZING POINTS OF VIEW** Knowing what you know about the Byzantine Empire, what are some of the pros and cons of conquering more territory? Fill in the table below.

Pros	Cons

ESSENTIAL QUESTION

What are the characteristics of a leader?

Code of Justinian

DIRECTIONS: Read the following excerpt and answer the accompanying questions.

EXPLORE THE CONTEXT: Justinian was the Byzantine emperor from 529 C.E. until 565 C.E. The Code of Justinian was a collection of laws and legal interpretations developed and written under his leadership.

PRIMARY SOURCE: LEGAL DOCUMENT

❝Justice is the set and constant purpose which gives to every man his due [what he deserves]. Jurisprudence is the knowledge of things divine and human, the science of the just and the unjust. . . .

The precepts of the law are these: to live honestly, to injure no one, and to give every man his due. The study of law consists of two branches, law public and law private. The former relates to the welfare of the Roman State; the latter to the advantage of the individual citizen. Of private law then we may say that it is of threefold origin, being collected from the precepts of nature, from those of the law of nations, or from those of the civil law of Rome. . . .

A statute is an enactment of the Roman people, which it used to make on the motion of a senatorial magistrate, as for instance a consul. . . . [W]hat the Emperor determines has the force of a statute, the people having conferred [granted] on him all their authority and power by the lex regia, which was passed concerning his office and authority. Consequently, whatever the Emperor settles by rescript, or decides in his judicial capacity, or ordains [orders] edicts [laws], is clearly a statute: and these are what are called constitutions. ❞

— from *The Institutes of Justinian,* c. 534 C.E.

VOCABULARY

jurisprudence: a system of law
precepts: general rules
welfare: well-being
threefold: three times as great
magistrate: official
rescript: a written answer of a Roman emperor to a legal inquiry
capacity: role

1 **DETERMINING CONTEXT** What is Justinian's purpose in creating this code? What evidence in the text supports your answer?

_____

_____

_____

_____

2 **SUMMARIZING** According to Justinian, what are the "precepts" of the code?

_____

_____

_____

_____

3 CIVICS According to Justinian, what are the three areas of origin of law?

_____

_____

_____

_____

4 **MAKE CONNECTIONS** In what way did the Roman emperor have more power than the president of the United States?

_____

_____

_____

_____

_____

Procopius on the Emperor Justinian

ESSENTIAL QUESTION

What are the characteristics of a leader?

DIRECTIONS: Read the following excerpt and answer the accompanying questions.

EXPLORE THE CONTEXT: Byzantine scholar Procopius, who died in 565 C.E., is considered the last major ancient historian. He traveled with the army of Eastern Roman Emperor Justinian I as a military adviser. This excerpt comes from Procopius's *Anecdota (Secret History)*, which was published after Procopius's death.

PRIMARY SOURCE: BOOK

> " This Emperor [Justinian], then, was deceitful, devious [tricky], false, hypocritical, two-faced, cruel, skilled in dissembling his thought, never moved to tears by either joy or pain, though he could summon them artfully at will when the occasion demanded, a liar always, not only offhand, but in writing, and when he swore sacred oaths to his subjects in their very hearing. Then he would immediately break his agreements and pledges, like the vilest of slaves, whom indeed only the fear of torture drives to confess their perjury. A faithless friend, he was a treacherous enemy, insane for murder and plunder [theft], quarrelsome and revolutionary, easily led to anything, but never willing to listen to good counsel, quick to plan mischief and carry it out, but finding even the hearing of anything good distasteful to his ears. . . .
>
> He had no scruples [misgivings] about appropriating other people's property, and did not even think any excuse necessary, legal or illegal, for confiscating what did not belong to him. And when it was his, he was more than ready to squander it in insane display, or give it as an unnecessary bribe to the barbarians. In short, he neither held on to any money himself nor let anyone else keep any: as if his reason were not avarice [greed], but jealousy of those who had riches. Driving all wealth from the country of the Romans in this manner, he became the cause of universal poverty. "

— Procopius, *Secret History,* c. 550 C.E.

VOCABULARY

deceitful: dishonest
dissembling: hiding
summon: to bid to come
perjury: false swearing
appropriating: taking without right
treacherous: dangerous
confiscating: taking away
squander: lose through negligence

1 **CONTRASTING** How does Procopius's view of Justinian differ with the impression you have of Justinian from his law code?

_____

_____

_____

_____

2 **ANALYZING SOURCES** What impact would Procopius's use of a long list to describe Justinian's characteristics have on the reader?

_____

_____

_____

_____

_____

3 CIVICS For what purpose do you think Procopius wrote this history of Justinian?

_____

_____

_____

_____

_____

4 **MAKE CONNECTIONS** Despite this description from Procopius, Justinian is remembered well—as a respectable, strong leader. Why do you think that is? What determines how a political leader is remembered?

_____

_____

_____

_____

_____

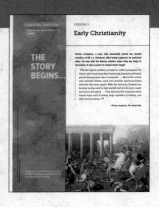

ESSENTIAL QUESTION

What are the characteristics of a leader?

As you gather evidence to answer the Essential Question, think about:

- the characteristics of Jesus and his disciples.
- how Jesus influenced the people around him.

My Notes

_____

_____

_____

_____

_____

_____

_____

_____

Early Christianity

DIRECTIONS: Search for evidence in Chapter 1, Lesson 3 to help you answer the following questions.

1 ┃ HISTORY ┃ Use the time line below to outline the relationship between Rome and the Jewish people.

63 B.C.E.

66 C.E.

70 C.E.

132 C.E.

700 C.E.

2 ┃ CIVICS ┃ How did Jews at Masada revolt against the Romans?

_____

_____

_____

_____

3 ANALYZING INTERACTIONS Use the graphic organizer below to describe the multiple reactions that Jews had to Roman rule.

Jewish Reactions to Roman Rule
•
•
•

4 DESCRIBING What are the basic Christian beliefs?

_____

_____

_____

_____

_____

_____

5 SUMMARIZING Use the following chart to summarize the roles of early Christian leaders in the development of Christianity.

Leader(s)	Role/Achievements
The Apostles	
Peter	
Paul	

Pilate's Letter to Herod

DIRECTIONS: Read the following excerpt and answer the accompanying questions.

EXPLORE THE CONTEXT: Pontius Pilate was the Roman official in charge of Jerusalem and Galilee, where Jesus was from, at the time of Jesus' crucifixion. Jesus was brought before Pilate, who sent him on to Herod. Although neither found him guilty, Pilate had Jesus crucified at the request of the people. The letter below is from a collection that dates to the 500s or 600s C.E. They were not written by Pilate himself and are best read as a dramatic recount of his life.

PRIMARY SOURCE: LETTER

"Pilate to Herod the Tetrarch: Peace.

KNOW and see, that in the day when thou didst deliver Jesus unto me, I took pity on myself, and testified by washing my hands (that I was innocent), concerning him who rose from the grave after three days, and had performed thy pleasure in him, for thou didst desire me to be associated with thee in his crucifixion. But I now learn from the executioners and from the soldiers who watched his sepulchre that he rose from the dead. And I have especially confirmed what was told me, that he appeared bodily in Galilee, to the same form, and with the same voice, and with the same doctrine [policy], and with the same disciples, not having changed in anything, but preaching with boldness his resurrection, and an everlasting kingdom. . . .

Now when Procla, my wife, heard that Jesus was risen, and had appeared in Galilee, she took with her Longinus the centurion and twelve soldiers, the same that had watched at the sepulchre, and went to greet the face of Christ, as if to a great spectacle, and saw him with his disciples.

Now while they were standing, and wondering, and gazing at him, he looked at them, and said to them, What is it? Do ye believe in me? Procla, know that in the covenant which God gave to the fathers, it is

VOCABULARY

Tetrach: a Roman governor
testified: stated
associated: connected
sepulchre: tomb
spectacle: unusual sight

. . . continued

said that every body which had perished [died] should live by means of my death, which ye have seen. And now, ye see that I live, whom ye crucified. And I suffered many things, till that I was laid in the sepulchre. But now, hear me, and believe in my Father—God who is in me. For I loosed the cords of death, and brake the gates of Sheol; and my coming shall be hereafter. **"**

— letter from Pilate to Herod

1 HISTORY What does the text mean when it says that Pilate washed his hands and "performed thy pleasure" in Jesus?

_____

_____

_____

_____

2 **ANALYZING SOURCES** Why does the author make a point of saying that Jesus rose from the dead with "the same form, and with the same voice, and with the same doctrine"?

_____

_____

_____

3 **INFERRING** Why might the author, who was not Pilate, have written this letter?

_____

_____

_____

4 **MAKE CONNECTIONS** Why might this source be considered unreliable as a historical resource? In what context would this source be reliable?

_____

_____

_____

What are the characteristics of a leader?

The Prodigal Son

DIRECTIONS: Read the following passage and answer the accompanying questions.

EXPLORE THE CONTEXT: Jesus often taught in parables, or stories with a lesson. The Parable of the Prodigal Son, also known as the Lost Son, is one of these parables. This parable was recorded by Luke, one of Jesus' apostles, and appears in the King James version of the Bible in Luke 15:11-32.

VOCABULARY

portion: individual share
substance: material possessions
riotous: excessive
famine: extreme scarcity of food
compassion: merciful kindness
intreated: earnestly requested
transgressed: sinned
harlots: prostitutes

PRIMARY SOURCE: SERMON

" 11 And he said, A certain man had two sons:

12 And the younger of them said to his father, Father, give me the portion of goods that falleth to me. And he divided unto them his living.

13 And not many days after the younger son gathered all together, and took his journey into a far country, and there wasted his substance with riotous living.

14 And when he had spent all, there arose a mighty famine in that land; and he began to be in want. . . .

17 And when he came to himself, he said, How many hired servants of my father's have bread enough and to spare, and I perish with hunger! . . .

20 And he arose, and came to his father. But when he was yet a great way off, his father saw him, and had compassion, and ran, and fell on his neck, and kissed him.

21 And the son said unto him, Father, I have sinned against heaven, and in thy sight, and am no more worthy to be called thy son.

22 But the father said to his servants, Bring forth the best robe, and put it on him; and put a ring on his hand, and shoes on his feet:

23 And bring hither [here] the fatted calf, and kill it; and let us eat, and be merry:

. . . continued

24 For this my son was dead, and is alive again; he was lost, and is found. And they began to be merry.

25 Now his elder son was in the field: and as he came and drew nigh to the house, he heard musick and dancing. . .

28 And he was angry, and would not go in: therefore came his father out, and intreated him.

29 And he answering said to his father, Lo, these many years do I serve thee, neither transgressed I at any time thy commandment: and yet thou never gavest me a kid, that I might make merry with my friends:

30 But as soon as this thy son was come, which hath devoured thy living with harlots, thou hast killed for him the fatted calf.

31 And he said unto him, Son, thou art ever with me, and all that I have is thine [yours].

32 It was meet [appropriate] that we should make merry, and be glad: for this thy brother was dead, and is alive again; and was lost, and is found. **"**

—Luke 15:11–32, c. 1st century C.E.

1 **EXPLAINING** Why is this an example of a parable?

_____

_____

_____

_____

_____

_____

2 **INFERRING** What message was Jesus trying to share with this parable?

_____

_____

_____

_____

_____

_____

_____

3 **ANALYZING POINTS OF VIEW** Why was one brother upset that his father threw a party for the other brother?

_____

_____

_____

_____

_____

_____

_____

4 **INFERRING** What does this primary source tell you about the character of Jesus?

_____

_____

_____

_____

_____

_____

_____

5 **MAKE CONNECTIONS** How can you relate the symbolism in this parable to the teachings of Christianity?

_____

_____

_____

_____

_____

_____

_____

_____

_____

_____

_____

_____

ESSENTIAL QUESTION

What are the characteristics of a leader?

As you gather evidence to answer the Essential Question, think about:

- the characteristics of the leaders of the early church.
- how Christianity emerged as a major world religion.

My Notes

_____

_____

_____

_____

_____

_____

_____

_____

_____

The Early Church

DIRECTIONS: Search for evidence in Chapter 1, Lesson 4 to help you answer the following questions.

1 **IDENTIFYING** What factors contributed to the spread of Christianity?

_____

_____

_____

_____

_____

_____

_____

2A **HISTORY** Why did Romans mistreat Christians?

_____

_____

_____

_____

_____

_____

2B **CIVICS** How did Christianity go from being a threat to being the official religion of the Roman Empire?

_____

_____

_____

_____

3 MAKE CONNECTIONS Why did you think groups of Christians in different regions began to practice Christianity differently?

_____

_____

_____

4 SUMMARIZING Use the graphic organizer below to describe the roles of the different members of the church hierarchy.

Patriarchs

Archbishops

Bishops

Priests

Laity

5 CITING TEXT EVIDENCE According to the chapter, from where did the pope claim his authority?

_____

_____

_____

The Edict of Milan

DIRECTIONS: Read the following excerpt and answer the accompanying questions.

EXPLORE THE CONTEXT: The Edict of Milan permanently established religious freedom. An edict is a law. The Edict of Milan outlined toleration for Christianity and other religions within the Roman Empire. The Edict was the outcome of a political agreement between the Roman emperors Constantine I and Licinius and was created in Milan in 313 C.E.

PRIMARY SOURCE: EDICT

" . . . without regard to any provisos in our former orders to you concerning the Christians, all who choose that religion are to be permitted, freely and absolutely, to remain in it, and not to be disturbed any ways, or molested [bothered]. And we thought fit to be thus special in the things committed to your charge, that you might understand that the indulgence which we have granted in matters of religion to the Christians is ample and unconditional; and perceive at the same time that the open and free exercise of their respective religions is granted to all others, as well as to the Christians. For it befits the well-ordered state and the tranquillity [peace] of our times that each individual be allowed, according to his own choice, to worship the Divinity; and we mean not to derogate aught from the honour due to any religion or its votaries. Moreover, with respect to the Christians, we formerly gave certain orders concerning the places appropriated for their religious assemblies; but now we will that all persons who have purchased such places, either from our exchequer [government official responsible for money] or from any one else, do restore them to the Christians, without money demanded or price claimed, and that this be performed peremptorily and unambiguously [clearly]; . . . And because it appears that, besides the places

VOCABULARY

provisos: conditions
indulgence: tolerance
ample: generously sufficient
befits: is proper for
derogate: detract
aught: anything at all
votaries: devoted followers
appropriated: set aside for
peremptorily: urgently

. . . continued

appropriated to religious worship, the Christians did possess other places, which belonged not to individuals, but to their society in general, that is, to their churches, we comprehend all such within the regulation aforesaid, and we will that you cause them all to be restored to the society or churches, and that without hesitation or controversy. "

1 CIVICS According to the edict, how will freedom of religion benefit society?

_____
_____
_____

2 INFERRING What might this edict tell you about the leadership of Constantine I?

_____
_____
_____

3 DETERMINING CONTEXT According to the text, what was happening to Christians at the time the edict was issued?

_____
_____
_____
_____

4 MAKE CONNECTIONS What central American document guarantees freedom of religion?

_____
_____
_____

ESSENTIAL QUESTION
What are the characteristics of a leader?

St. Augustine's *The City of God*

DIRECTIONS: Read the following excerpt and answer the accompanying questions.

EXPLORE THE CONTEXT: Augustine of Hippo, later known as St. Augustine, was a Catholic bishop in Africa in the late 300s and early 400s C.E. His book *The City of God* was, in part, a response to the weakening of the Western Roman Empire. In *The City of God,* Augustine proposed the existence of a spiritual city, separate and distinct from the cities that existed on Earth.

PRIMARY SOURCE: BOOK

66 But remember that, in recounting [telling] these things, I have still to address myself to ignorant men; so ignorant, indeed, as to give birth to the common saying, "Drought and Christianity go hand in hand." There are indeed some among them who are thoroughly well educated men, and have a taste for history, in which the things I speak of are open to their observation; but in order to irritate the uneducated masses against us, they feign ignorance of these events, and do what they can to make the vulgar believe that those disasters, which in certain places and at certain times uniformly befall mankind, are the result of Christianity, which is being everywhere diffused, and is possessed of a renown and brilliancy which quite eclipse their own gods. Let them then, along with us, call to mind with what various and repeated disasters the prosperity of Rome was blighted, before ever Christ had come in the flesh, and before His name had been blazoned among the nations with that glory which they vainly grudge [resent]. Let them, if they can, defend their gods in this article, since they maintain that they worship them in order to be preserved from these disasters, which they now impute to us if they suffer in the least degree. For why did these gods permit the disasters I am to speak of to fall on their worshippers before the preaching of Christ's name offended them, and put an end to their sacrifices? 99

—from *The City of God* by Aurelius Augustine, Bishop of Hippo

VOCABULARY

feign: pretend
vulgar: uneducated
befall: happen to
diffused: spread
renown: fame
blighted: damaged
blazoned: proclaimed
impute: complain

1 **ANALYZING SOURCES** According to Augustine, who do "ignorant men" blame for the troubles of the Western Roman Empire?

_____

_____

_____

_____

2 **ANALYZING PERSPECTIVES** Does Augustine believe this blame is justified? Why or why not?

_____

_____

_____

_____

_____

_____

_____

3 **IDENTIFYING CAUSES** According to Augustine, why do these "ignorant men" blame Christianity?

_____

_____

_____

_____

4 HISTORY Augustine of Hippo is respected as an early leader of the Christian Church. Based on this excerpt, what qualities did Augustine possess as a leader?

_____

_____

_____

_____

ESSENTIAL QUESTION

What are the characteristics of a leader?

As you gather evidence to answer the Essential Question, think about:

- the characteristics of European leaders such as Charlemagne and Patrick of Ireland.
- how these leaders influenced Europe.

My Notes

_____

_____

_____

_____

_____

_____

_____

_____

A Christian Europe

DIRECTIONS: Search for evidence in Chapter 1, Lesson 5 to help you answer the following questions.

1 | HISTORY | Use the graphic organizer below to list the differences that led to the schism between the Western and Eastern Christian churches.

Western Christian Church	Eastern Christian Church

2A IDENTIFYING What is an icon?

_____

_____

_____

_____

_____

2B **IDENTIFYING CAUSES** Why did Emperor Leo III order the removal of icons from churches?

_____

_____

_____

_____

3 **SUMMARIZING** What role did monks and nuns play in Christian Europe?

_____

_____

_____

_____

4 **ANALYZING** How do the actions of Cyril and his brother Methodius show how religion can affect other aspects of society?

_____

_____

_____

_____

5 GEOGRAPHY Who was largely responsible for spreading Christianity to England and Ireland?

_____

_____

_____

_____

What are the characteristics of a leader?

The Vita Karoli Magni

DIRECTIONS: Read the following excerpt and answer the accompanying questions.

EXPLORE THE CONTEXT: Eginhard was a Frankish scholar and courtier. He was a dedicated servant of Charlemagne and his son Louis the Pious. The most famous of Eginhard's works is his biography of Charlemagne entitled *The Life of Charlemagne,* or *Vita Karoli Magni.* The book gives a lot of direct information about Charlemagne's life and character. It was written sometime between 817 and 830 C.E.

PRIMARY SOURCE: BOOK

❝He cherished the Church of St. Peter the Apostle at Rome above all other holy and sacred places, and heaped its treasury with a vast wealth of gold, silver, and precious stones. He sent great and countless gifts to the popes; and throughout his whole reign the wish that he had nearest at heart was to re-establish the ancient authority of the city of Rome under his care and by his influence, and to defend and protect the Church of St. Peter, and to beautify and enrich it out of his own store above all other churches. Although he held it in such veneration, he only repaired to Rome to pay his vows and make his supplications [prayers] four times during the whole forty-seven years that he reigned. ❞

— Eginhard, *The Life of Charlemagne*

VOCABULARY

vast: great
reign: period of rule
influence: the power to cause effect

enrich: to add desirable qualities
veneration: respect or awe

1 **INFERRING** Based on this excerpt, how do you think Charlemagne showed his respect or awe for people and places?

_____

_____

_____

2 **ANALYZING** Would you say that Charlemagne was a devoted Christian? What evidence can you cite from the text?

_____

_____

_____

_____

_____

_____

3 HISTORY How does Charlemagne's attitude toward the Church compare to that of Constantine, based on the Edict of Milan you read earlier?

_____

_____

_____

_____

_____

4 **MAKE CONNECTIONS** Why do you think ancient and medieval government officials would want to support religious leaders?

_____

_____

_____

The Confession of St. Patrick

DIRECTIONS: Read the following excerpt and answer the accompanying questions.

EXPLORE THE CONTEXT: Patrick was born in Britain around 390 C.E. According to *The Confession of St. Patrick*, he was captured by pirates and taken as a slave to Ireland at the age of 16. After six years, he escaped to Britain and became a cleric. He returned to Ireland as a bishop around 432 C.E., converting many and establishing the first Irish church at Armagh. He died in the city of Down. He wrote *The Confession of St. Patrick* as a response to attacks on his integrity. Saint Patrick's Day is observed on March 17, the supposed date of his death.

PRIMARY SOURCE: BOOK

❝I was at that time about sixteen years of age. I did not, indeed, know the true God; and I was taken into captivity in Ireland with many thousands of people, according to our deserts, for quite drawn away from God, we did not keep his precepts, nor were we obedient to our priests who used to remind us of our salvation. And the Lord brought down on us the fury of his being and scattered us among many nations, even to the ends of the earth, where I, in my smallness, am now to be found among foreigners.

2 And there the Lord opened my mind to an awareness of my unbelief, in order that, even so late, I might remember my transgressions and turn with all my heart to the Lord my God, who had regard for my insignificance and pitied my youth and ignorance. And he watched over me before I knew him, and before I learned sense or even distinguished between good and evil, and he protected me, and consoled me as a father would his son.

3 Therefore, indeed, I cannot keep silent, nor would it be proper, so many favours and graces has the Lord deigned to bestow on me in the land of my captivity. For after chastisement from God, and

VOCABULARY

captivity: imprisonment
fury: rage
insignificance: unimportance
distinguished: differentiated

favours: gracious acts of kindness
deigned: stooped
bestow: to give as a gift
chastisement: punishment

. . . continued

recognizing him, our way to repay him is to exalt him and confess his wonders before every nation under heaven. **"**

—St. Patrick, *The Confession of Saint Patrick*, c. 432–500 c.e.

1 COMPARING How would you compare the way Patrick writes about himself to the way Caesar Augustus wrote about himself at the beginning of this chapter?

_____

_____

_____

_____

2 HISTORY Why do you think Patrick was made a saint by the church?

_____

_____

_____

3 ANALYZING POINTS OF VIEW From Patrick's point of view, why is he teaching Christianity to others?

_____

_____

_____

_____

4 MAKE CONNECTIONS Why is St. Patrick's Day still relevant today?

_____

_____

_____

_____

ESSENTIAL QUESTION

What are the characteristics of a leader?

1 Think About It

Review the Supporting Questions that you developed at the beginning of the chapter. Review the evidence that you gathered in Chapter 1. Were you able to answer each Supporting Question?

If there was not enough evidence to answer your Supporting Questions, what additional evidence do you think you need to consider?

_____

_____

_____

2 Organize Your Evidence

Use a chart like the one below to organize the evidence you will use to support your findings about leadership characteristics.

Leader	Area of Rule or Influence	Main Characteristics	Source of information to cite as evidence	How characteristics influenced society

3 Write About It

A position statement related to the Essential Question should reflect your conclusion about the evidence. Write a Position Statement for the ESSENTIAL QUESTION: *What are the characteristics of a leader?*

_____

_____

_____

_____

_____

_____

_____

_____

_____

4 Talk About It

Work in a small group to present your position statement and evidence. Gather feedback from your classmates before you write your final conclusion. You may choose to refine your position statement after you have discussed it with your classmates. Group members should listen to one another's arguments, ask questions, and offer constructive advice about the statement.

5 Connect to the Essential Question

On a separate piece of paper, write a play that helps to answer the ESSENTIAL QUESTION: *What are the characteristics of a leader?* Choose three or four leaders that you learned about in this chapter to be the main characters, choose a setting, and think of a conflict or problem that they face. Then create interactions that show the characteristics of the different leaders you are writing about. How do those characteristics influence the way they resolve conflicts or solve problems? Through your play, readers should be able to understand the characteristics of the leaders and how they influenced people around them. Remember to be respectful when writing about religious leaders or topics.

CITIZENSHIP
TAKING ACTION

MAKE CONNECTIONS Leaders influence our society in many ways. Who are your government and religious leaders? Research some leaders in your area and examine how their characteristics have influenced public policy or shaped your community. Is there a leader who impresses you? Is there a leader who disappoints you?

DIRECTIONS: Pick a leader to whom you would like to write a letter. You can thank him or her for leadership qualities you believe he or she has demonstrated or request specific actions be taken on behalf of your community. Share your letter with the class.

_____

_____

_____

_____

_____

_____

_____

_____

_____

_____

_____

_____

_____

_____

_____

1 **EXPLORING CONTEXT** How do the letters on many deniers help you understand the society in which they were printed?

_____

_____

_____

_____

2 **DETERMINING MEANING** Why might the detail of a temple or religious symbol be important on a coin of this period?

_____

_____

_____

_____

_____

3 **HISTORICAL INFERENCE** What inference can you make about a nation's ruler and land from a coin stamped with his image?

_____

_____

_____

_____

4 **DRAWING CONCLUSIONS** What conclusions can you draw about a civilization that uses coins rather than a barter system for exchanging goods?

_____

_____

_____

_____

_____

Why does conflict develop?

The Oseberg Ship

DIRECTIONS: Look at the image and answer the accompanying questions.

EXPLORE THE CONTEXT: The oak vessel in this image is an actual Viking ship now displayed in a museum. It was used by the Vikings in the 700s to 800s C.E. The ship has oar holes for oarsmen so that it can be rowed. It also has a mast for a sail so that it can use wind power to navigate. The prows, or fronts, of many of these ships were carved with ornate decorations, one of the most common of which was a curled serpent. These beautiful carvings were likely the work of skilled artists, making them very expensive to create.

PRIMARY SOURCE: ARTIFACT

2 IDENTIFYING EFFECTS According to the law, what is the punishment for missing one of the king's meetings?

_____

_____

_____

_____

_____

_____

3 HISTORY What can you tell from the document about the system the king used to communicate with the people of his kingdom?

_____

_____

_____

_____

_____

_____

_____

_____

4 EVALUATING EVIDENCE What can you tell about civil society, or the relationship between government and citizens, from reading this document?

_____

_____

_____

_____

_____

_____

_____

ESSENTIAL QUESTION
Why does conflict develop?

Richard of Ely on Tax Collection

DIRECTIONS: Study the following excerpt and answer the accompanying questions.

EXPLORE THE CONTEXT: Historians believe that this document was created in 1178. The author is Richard, son of Bishop Nigel of Ely. Both Richard and his father were important officials at the exchequer. Richard created the document as part of his work for the government. The "Conquest" he refers to is the conquest of England by William of Normandy in 1066 C.E. William is credited with introducing European feudalism to England.

SECONDARY SOURCE: BOOK

" VII. By whom, or for what purpose, the testing of silver was instituted.

In the primitive state of the kingdom after the Conquest, as we have learned from our fathers, not weights of gold or silver, but solely victuals were paid to the kings from their lands, from which the necessaries for the daily use of the royal household were furnished. And those who had been appointed for this purpose knew how much came from the separate estates. . . . This arrangement, however, continued during the whole time of King William I, and up to the time of King Henry, his son; so that I myself saw some people who had seen victuals carried at stated times from the estates of the crown to the court: and the officials of the royal household knew from which counties corn and from which different kinds of meat, or fodder for horses, or any other necessary things, were due. . . . But as time went on, when the same king was occupied across the channel and in remote places, in calming the tumults of war, it came about that the sum necessary for meeting these expenses was paid in ready money. "

—from *The Dialogue Concerning the Exchequer. First Book, Chapter VII,* 1178 C.E.

VOCABULARY

Conquest: the triumph of William the Conqueror
victuals: food
tumults: chaos

exchequer: the government office responsible for collecting taxes and paying the king's bills

2 ECONOMICS How would you characterize the economy of Andover based on the details in the *Domesday Book* entry for the area?

_____

_____

_____

_____

_____

_____

3 INFERRING What do you think was William I's purpose for creating document?

_____

_____

_____

_____

_____

_____

_____

4 RELATING EVENTS Can you think of how our government accounts for the people, property, and goods that exist in each town today? How is it similar to or different from the *Domesday Book*?

_____

_____

_____

_____

_____

_____

_____

ESSENTIAL QUESTION
Why does conflict develop?

VOCABULARY

Omnipotent: all-powerful, in this case, God

heathen: any non-Christian person

Forgiveness of Sins

DIRECTIONS: Study the following passage and answer the accompanying questions.

EXPLORE THE CONTEXT: Pope Leo IV wrote this passage in 847 C.E. He issued the statement to the Frankish Army to encourage them to begin a Crusade to the Holy Land. Their enemy in the battle is the Muslims, who govern most of the lands of the Middle East.

PRIMARY SOURCE: PAPAL STATEMENT

66 Now we hope that none of you will be slain, but we wish you to know that the kingdom of heaven will be given as a reward to those who shall be killed in this war. For the Omnipotent knows that they lost their lives fighting for the truth of the faith, for the preservation of their country, and the defense of Christians. And therefore God will give then, the reward which we have named. 99

—from *Forgiveness of Sins for Those Who Dies in Battle With the Heathen,* 847 C.E.

1 **ANALYZING SOURCES** What is Pope Leo IV offering the soldiers who set out on a Crusade?

_____

_____

_____

_____

_____

_____

_____

_____

_____

_____

1 **ANALYZING SOURCES** How is the University of Paris connected to the University of Heidelberg?

_____

_____

_____

2 **DRAWING CONCLUSIONS** What are the four schools within the University of Heidelberg? What can you tell about the culture from this structure?

_____

_____

_____

3 HISTORY What historical factors might have led Rupert to model the University of Heidelberg after the existing University of Paris?

_____

_____

_____

4 **IDENTIFYING EFFECTS** How will the structure of the university directly impact Germany?

_____

_____

The Late Middle Ages

DIRECTIONS: Search for evidence in Chapter 2, Lesson 5 to help you complete the following items.

1 **HISTORY** Complete the chart about the Black Death.

ESSENTIAL QUESTION

Why does conflict develop?

As you gather evidence to answer the Essential Question, think about:

- how government responsibilities change during times of crisis.
- the ways that communities create scapegoats when things go wrong.
- how war changes the interactions between nations and religions.

My Notes

_____

_____

_____

_____

_____

_____

_____

_____

_____

_____

Who was impacted by the Black Death?	
What happened to wages as a result of the plague?	
When did the plague hit Europe the worst?	
Where did the plague begin? How did the plague get to Europe?	
How many people died in Asia and Europe from the plague?	

2 ECONOMICS What were some of the economic consequences of the bubonic plague?

_____

_____

_____

_____

3 **ANALYZING KEY IDEAS AND DETAILS** How did the Great Schism weaken the leadership of the Church?

_____

_____

_____

4 **IDENTIFYING CAUSE AND EFFECT** Complete the organizer to show factors that led to the Spanish Inquisition and its effects.

CAUSE		EFFECT
	SPANISH INQUISITION	

ESSENTIAL QUESTION
Why does conflict develop?

Jacques Lenfant on the Council of Constance

DIRECTIONS: Study the following excerpt and answer the accompanying questions.

EXPLORE THE CONTEXT: The Council of Constance was the official meeting that ended the Great Schism. It occurred from 1414 until 1418. The outcome of the council was to have all the rival popes step down and for the bishops to elect one pope that all of them could agree upon. The meeting put to rest the leadership conflict in the Roman Catholic Church.

VOCABULARY

oblig'd: grateful

SECONDARY SOURCE: BOOK

❝Historical Dissertation on the Fifth Edition of the ACTS of the Council of Constance

The Curious Art of Printing was unknown at the Time of the Council of Constance; for it was not till twenty or thirty Years after, that all Europe was oblig'd for this Present to Germany. Therefore 'tis no wonder that Acts of such Importance, as those of this famous Council, were bury'd in the Dust of publick and private Libraries. Nor was it till the latter End of the 15th Century, that any body took it into their Heads to bring them out to the Light. ❞

— Jacques Lenfant, *The History of the Council of Constance,* 1714

1　**IDENTIFYING CAUSES** According to the author, why had the details of the Council not been shared before this writing?

_____

_____

_____

_____

2 **ASSESSING CREDIBILITY** Who is the author of the passage? Why is his identity important to understanding the passage?

_____

_____

_____

_____

3 **ANALYZING SOURCES** What type of document is this? What details in the passage help you identify when the passage was written?

_____

_____

_____

4 **INFERRING** The _History of the Council of Constance_ was written in 1765, while the Council occurred in 1414–1418. Why did it take so long for someone to write this history?

_____

_____

_____

_____

ESSENTIAL QUESTION

Why does conflict develop?

VOCABULARY

straights: difficulties
idleness: laziness or unemployment
ordain: order
liveries: the business of vehicles for hire

meed: a share or reward
statute: law

Statutes of the Realm

DIRECTIONS: Study the following excerpt and answer the accompanying questions.

EXPLORE THE CONTEXT: The passage is a law from *Statutes of the Realm*, written in England in 1351.

PRIMARY SOURCE: LEGAL DOCUMENT

Statute of Laborers; 1351

"Because a great part of the people and especially of the workmen and servants has now died in that pestilence [plague], some, seeing the straights of the masters and the scarcity of servants, are not willing to serve unless they receive excessive wages, and others, rather than through labour to gain their living, prefer to beg in idleness: We, . . . ordain that every man and woman of our kingdom of England, . . . whether bond or free, who is able bodied and below the age of sixty years, not living from trade nor carrying on a fixed craft, . . . and not serving another, if he, considering his station, be sought after to serve in a suitable service, he shall be bound to serve him who has seen fit so to seek after him; and he shall take only the wages liveries, meed or salary which, in the places where he sought to serve, were accustomed to be paid in the twentieth year of our reign of England, or the five or six common years next preceding."

—Ernest F. Henderson, *Select Historical Documents of the Middle Ages*

1 **ANALYZING SOURCES** What does the Statute of Laborers require?

_____

_____

_____

2 **DETERMINING CONTEXT** When was the law written? What events were happening in Europe at that time that help you understand the law?

_____

_____

_____

3 **ECONOMICS** What specific item does the statute demand related to wages? From this detail, what can you tell about how the Black Death impacted the labor market?

_____

_____

_____

4 **INFERRING** What detail in the passage suggests that the Black Death had given serfs greater power to change their station in society?

_____

_____

_____

ESSENTIAL QUESTION

Why does conflict develop?

1 Think About It

Review the supporting questions you developed at the opening of the chapter. Review the evidence you found in Chapter 2. Were you able to answer each of your Supporting Questions?

If you didn't find enough evidence to answer your Supporting Questions, what do you think you need to consider?

_____

_____

_____

_____

_____

_____

2 Organize Your Evidence

Use charts like the one below to organize the evidence you will use to support your position statement.

Conflict	Evidence

3 Talk About It

Discuss the evidence you have gathered with a small group or partner. Check your group's understanding of the structures in the Middle Ages that led to conflict and answer any questions members may have. Consider any additional advice or input they may have.

4 Connect to the Essential Question

On a separate piece of paper, write an expository essay that answers the Essential Question: *Why does conflict develop?* In your essay, explain how kingdoms, the Church, as well as the social structures of feudalism and guilds, contributed to conflict in Europe.

CITIZENSHIP
TAKING ACTION

MAKE CONNECTIONS Ideas about citizenship changed during the Middle Ages. For the first time, rights of citizens were recognized. Townspeople were given the right to buy and sell property. In England, the Magna Carta protected rights such as the right to a trial by jury. In the United States, the Bill of Rights lists specific rights guaranteed to all U.S. citizens. Some of these rights came from the Magna Carta.

DIRECTIONS: Look up the rights protected by the Bill of Rights. Choose the three you believe are most important and create a "Know Your Rights" campaign poster explaining those three rights. On your poster, use a combination of text and graphics to identify each right and explain what it means.

_____

_____

_____

_____

_____

_____

_____

_____

_____

_____

_____

_____

Islamic Civilization

ESSENTIAL QUESTION
How do belief systems influence society and government?

Think about how this question might relate to the development of early Islamic civilization.

TALK ABOUT IT   COLLABORATE

Discuss with a partner what type of information you would need to know to answer this question. For example, one question might be: What are the most important teachings of the Quran?

DIRECTIONS: Now write down three additional questions that you need to answer to be able to explain why and how Islam developed.

MY RESEARCH QUESTIONS

Supporting Question 1:

_____

_____

Supporting Question 2:

_____

_____

Supporting Question 3:

_____

_____

ESSENTIAL QUESTION

How do belief systems influence society and government?

As you gather evidence to answer the Essential Question, think about:

- what life was like on the Arabian Peninsula.
- why people followed Muhammad.
- how the Arabs' tribal society changed with the rise of Islam.
- the teachings of the Quran.

My Notes

A New Faith

DIRECTIONS: Search for evidence in Chapter 3, Lesson 1 to help you answer the following questions.

1 **EXPLAINING** What is the significance of Makkah to Islamic society?

_____

_____

_____

_____

2 **CITING TEXT EVIDENCE** How were the beliefs Arabs held prior to Islam carried over into this new religion?

_____

_____

_____

_____

_____

3 **ECONOMICS** How did trade between Arabs and other civilizations help Islam to develop?

_____

_____

_____

_____

_____

4 IDENTIFYING CAUSES Why was Muhammad inspired to preach to other Arabs?

_____

_____

_____

_____

5 INTEGRATING VISUAL INFORMATION Look at the photographs of the Kaaba. What do these photographs illustrate about Islam and Muslims?

_____

_____

_____

_____

6 UNDERSTANDING CHRONOLOGY Complete the graphic organizer below with the significant events that contributed to Muhammad's rise as a prophet and the development of the Quran.

Muhammad wins the support of the poor.		

		Islamic scholars then create a code of law called shari'ah.

VOCABULARY

russet: a shade of reddish-brown
serene: peaceful
trappings: decorations or ornaments
humble: plain
frolic: to play, skip, or romp
litter: a long seat with rods surrounded by curtains that is used to carry one person
kindred: family

The Song of Maisuna

DIRECTIONS: Read the following poem and answer the accompanying questions.

EXPLORE THE CONTENT: A great deal of literature came from Muslim men and women of this era. This poem was written c. 661–680 C.E. by a woman named Maisuna, who was a wife of a leader of Islam after the death of Muhammad. The poem brings the reader into a typical moment of Arabian life.

PRIMARY SOURCE: POEM

"The russet suit of camel's hair,

With spirits light, and eye serene,

Is dearer to my bosom far

Than all the trappings of a queen.

The humble tent and murmuring breeze

That whistles thro' its fluttering wall,

My unaspiring fancy please

Better than towers and splendid halls.

Th' attendant colts that bounding fly

And frolic by the litter's side,

Are dearer in Maisuna's eye

Than gorgeous mules in all their pride.

The watch-dog's voice that bays whene'er

A stranger seeks his master's cot,

Sounds sweeter in Maisuna's ear

Than yonder trumpet's long-drawn note.

The rustic youth unspoilt by art,

Son of my kindred, poor but free,

Will ever to Maisuna's heart

Be dearer, pamper'd fool, than thee."

—Maisuna, wife to the Caliph Mowiah

1a **ANALYZING** Why does the author use phrases such as "Is dearer to my bosom far/Than all the trappings of a queen" and "Sounds sweeter in Maisuna's ear/Than yonder trumpet's long-drawn note"?

_____

_____

_____

_____

_____

1b **COMPARING** What are some other comparisons the author uses to express her feelings about the world around her?

_____

_____

_____

_____

_____

2 **DETERMINING CONTEXT** What words and phrases does the author use to help the reader understand the time and place?

_____

_____

_____

_____

_____

3 **INFERRING** What is the theme of the poem?

_____

_____

_____

_____

_____

ESSENTIAL QUESTION

How do belief systems influence society and government?

Islam and Charity

DIRECTIONS: Read the following excerpt and answer the accompanying questions.

EXPLORE THE CONTENT: The following text is from "The Five Principles of Islam and their Significance." It specifically explains Islam's final principle, zakat, or the giving of alms.

SECONDARY SOURCE: PERIODICAL

66 Now I come to the last and fifth principle of Islam, which has been promulgated [declared] by the Holy Qur-an in the terms of Zakat (poor-rates) or Sadaquat (alms). Every Muslim is expected to take a stock of his savings every year and to disburse [hand out] 2 1/2 per cent. of this as "alms." Charity in Islam takes two different forms: one is optional and the other compulsory [required], which is also called zakat. When asked as to what was the ultimate object of zakat, the Holy Prophet replied that it was a means whereby the rich had to give something out of their wealth for the help of those who are in need. The Holy Qur-an has laid down eight different purposes for the expenditure [spending] of this zakat money. It says: 'Alms are only for the poor, the needy, the officials appointed over them, those whose hearts are made inclined to truth, the ransoming of captives, those in debt, in the way of Allah and the wayfarer.'

It is Islam that has given charity the prestige [respect] and form of an institution. Before the advent [founding] of Islam the followers of other religions used to do charitable deeds on their own personal fancies and had no organization. But the Holy Prophet, whose aim was to systemize the religion and make it a living force in the civilization of mankind, laid down rules and regulations for charity, so that the general welfare of the society may be achieved. 99

—from "The Five Principles of Islam and their Significance" by Maulvi Mustafakhan, *The Islamic Review,* Vol. IX No. 6 (June-July 1921)

VOCABULARY

optional: voluntary

ultimate: essential

inclined: tend to take a particular action

fancies: desires or whims

institution: organization or society

systemize: to develop a method, order, or regularity

1a CIVICS Who is expected to pay zakat?

_____

_____

1b INFERRING Why do you think this group is singled out for observing this principle?

_____

_____

_____

_____

2 DESCRIBING What are some of the purposes of zakat?

_____

_____

_____

_____

3 CIVICS What is the larger benefit to paying zakat?

_____

_____

_____

_____

4 ANALYZING Explain why Mustafakhan believes "It is Islam that has given charity the prestige [respect] and form of an institution."

_____

_____

_____

5 INFERRING Why is zakat such an important principle in the Islamic faith?

_____

_____

_____

_____

ESSENTIAL QUESTION

How do belief systems influence society and government?

As you gather evidence to answer the Essential Question, think about:

- how the practices of Islam spread throughout the region.
- how the various Islamic leaders treated non-Muslims.
- how the first four caliphs changed and improved Islamic culture.
- how an Islamic state changed under various dynasties.

My Notes

The Spread of Islam

DIRECTIONS: Search for evidence in Chapter 3, Lesson 2 to help you answer the following questions.

1 EXPLAINING What was the goal of the first four caliphs?

2 CITING TEXT EVIDENCE What evidence in the text supports the idea that Byzantine and Persian policies helped Muslims create a large empire?

3 **COMPARING** Complete the Venn diagram.

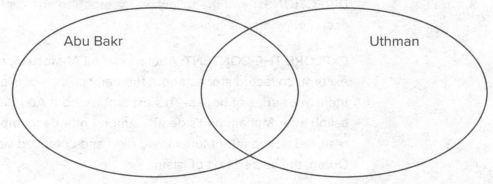

Abu Bakr   Uthman

4 **IDENTIFYING CAUSES** Why did Islam split into two similar but opposing groups?

_____

_____

_____

5 **DIFFERENTIATING** In the graphic organizer below, describe the major characteristics of each of the three Muslim empires.

Empire	Characteristics of the Empire			
Ottoman Empire				
Safavid Empire				
Mughal Empire				

ESSENTIAL QUESTION

How do belief systems influence society and government?

Masu'di on the First Caliph

DIRECTIONS: Read the following excerpt and answer the accompanying questions.

EXPLORE THE CONTENT: Abul Hasan Ali Al-Masu'di, author of this excerpt, collected stories about the early caliphs of Islam and published them in a series of books. This excerpt is about Abu Bakr, the first caliph after Muhammad's death. Among other accomplishments, he restored peace after Muhammad died and compiled verses of the Quran, the sacred text of Islam.

SECONDARY SOURCE: BOOK

66 Abu Bakr surpassed all the Muhammadans in his austerity, his frugality, and the simplicity of his life and outward appearance. During his rule he wore but a single linen garment and a cloak. In this simple dress he gave audience to the chiefs of the noblest Arab tribes and to the kings of Yemen. The latter appeared before him dressed in richest robes, covered with gold embroideries and wearing splendid crowns. But at sight of the Caliph, shamed by his mingling of pious humility and earnest gravity, they followed his example and renounced their gorgeous attire. 99

— Abul Hasan Ali Al-Masu'di, *The Book of Golden Meadows,* c. 940 C.E.

VOCABULARY

surpassed: went beyond

frugality: thriftiness

pious: holy; moral

gravity: seriousness

renounced: gave up

1a **ANALYZING POINTS OF VIEW** What is the author's opinion of Abu Bakr?

_____

_____

1b CITING TEXT EVIDENCE What evidence in the excerpt supports your claim?

_____

_____

_____

2 ANALYZING INDIVIDUALS Why does the author compare Abu Bakr to the chiefs?

_____

_____

_____

_____

3 ANALYZING SOURCES What phrase from the excerpt illustrates the author's claim that Abu Bakr was frugal?

_____

_____

_____

_____

4 CIVICS Why did the chiefs change the way they dressed?

_____

_____

_____

_____

5 INFERRING What can you infer about Abu Bakr's character?

_____

_____

_____

_____

ESSENTIAL QUESTION

How do belief systems influence society and government?

Geography and the Ottoman Empire

DIRECTIONS: Look at the following map and answer the accompanying questions.

EXPLORE THE CONTEXT: Islamic civilization spread through Europe and the Middle East during the Ottoman Empire. The map below, made in 1898, shows the spread of Islamic civilization. Use this map, along with other maps in your Student Edition, to help you answer the questions.

1 **IDENTIFYING CAUSES** Why did various rulers seeks to conquer neighboring regions?

_____

_____

_____

_____

_____

2 **USING MAPS** How did the location of the empire assist in its expansion?

_____

_____

_____

_____

_____

3 GEOGRAPHY Why did Cairo and Baghdad likely grow into large cities?

_____

_____

_____

_____

_____

ESSENTIAL QUESTION

How do belief systems influence society and government?

As you gather evidence to answer the Essential Question, think about:

- the development of trade in the region.
- how social groups were structured.
- contributions made by Muslims to mathematics, science, medicine, and the arts.

My Notes

_____

_____

_____

_____

_____

_____

_____

_____

Life in the Islamic World

DIRECTIONS: Search for evidence in Chapter 3, Lesson 3 to help you answer the following questions.

1 **EXPLAINING CAUSES** What contributed to the success of Muslim traders?

_____

_____

_____

_____

_____

_____

_____

2 **CITING TEXT EVIDENCE** How did mosques contribute to Islamic society?

_____

_____

_____

_____

_____

_____

3 **COMPARING** In the graphic organizer below, describe how life differed between cities and villages in the Muslim world.

Muslim City	Muslim Village

4 **EXPLAINING ISSUES** How did Islamic law protect enslaved people?

_____

_____

5 **IDENTIFYING** Complete the following chart to show the types of contributions Muslims made in the fields of medicine, science and mathematics, literature, and architecture.

Person	Field	Contribution
Al-Razi		
Mamun		
Omar Khayyam		
Shah Jahan		

ESSENTIAL QUESTION
How do belief systems influence society and government?

The Poetry of Omar Khayyam

DIRECTIONS: Read the following poem and answer the accompanying questions.

EXPLORE THE CONTENT: Omar Khayyam is one of the most famous authors of early Islam. In this poem, Khayyam explores a large topic—life—in very few sentences.

PRIMARY SOURCE: POEM

>"Nothing in this world of ours
>Flows as we would have it flow;
>What avail, then, careful hours,
>Thought and trouble, tears and woe?
>Through the shrouded veil of earth,
>Life's rich colors gleaming bright,
>Though in truth of little worth,
>Yet allure with meteor light.
>Life is torture and suspense;
>Thought is sorrow—drive it hence!
>With no will of mine I came,
>With no will depart the same."
>
>— Omar Khayyam, "The Vanity of Regret," c. 1100

VOCABULARY

vanity: pride, conceit
avail: benefit
shrouded: covered

allure: lit up
depart: leave

1 ANALYZING POINTS OF VIEW Why does Khayyam most likely use the word "ours" in the first line of the poem?

_____

_____

_____

_____

_____

_____

2 INFERRING What does the author mean by the lines "With no will of mine I came,/With no will depart the same."?

_____

_____

_____

_____

3 ANALYZING SOURCES Which pairs of lines from the poem suggests that people experience both good and bad times throughout their lives?

_____

_____

_____

_____

_____

4a ANALYZING POINTS OF VIEW Overall, what is the speaker's opinion about life?

_____

_____

_____

_____

4b IDENTIFYING PERSPECTIVES What evidence from the poem supports that claim?

_____

_____

_____

_____

_____

How do belief systems influence society and government?

Art of the Muslim World

DIRECTIONS: Look at the artwork and answer the accompanying questions.

EXPLORE THE CONTEXT: Early Muslims contributed greatly to the artwork of the era. Some of these pieces, such as this section of the Taj Mahal, built in the mid-1600s, still exist.

PRIMARY SOURCE: ART

1a DESCRIBING Describe the image shown in the artwork.

_____

_____

_____

_____

1b **INFERRING** Why might no living creatures be shown in this artwork?

_____

_____

_____

_____

_____

_____

2 **HISTORY** What does this artwork tell you about the artists of the time period?

_____

_____

_____

_____

_____

_____

3 **DRAWING CONCLUSIONS** What does this artwork tell you about the principles of early Islam?

_____

_____

_____

_____

_____

_____

ESSENTIAL QUESTION

How do belief systems influence society and government?

1 Think About It

Review the supporting questions that you developed at the beginning of the chapter. Review the evidence that you gathered in Chapter 3. Were you able to answer each Supporting Question?

If there was not enough evidence to answer your Supporting Questions, what additional evidence do you think you need to consider?

_____

_____

_____

_____

2 Organize Your Evidence

Use a chart like the one below to organize the evidence you will use to support your position statement.

Source of information	Specific evidence from the source to cite	How evidence helps support my Position Statement	Column Head Title

❸ Write About It

A position statement related to the Essential Question should reflect your conclusion about the evidence. Write a position statement for the ESSENTIAL QUESTION: *How do belief systems influence society and government?*

_____

_____

_____

_____

_____

❹ Talk About It

Work in a small group to present your position statement and evidence. Gather feedback from your classmates before you write your final conclusion. You may choose to refine your position statement after you have discussed it with your classmates. Group members should listen to each other's arguments, ask questions, and offer constructive advice about the statement.

❺ Connect to the Essential Question

Develop a visual essay to present your position statement and the evidence that supports it. Draw the images or choose photos and art from appropriate Web sites to illustrate the evidence. Include captions explaining how the evidence supports your position statement.

CITIZENSHIP
TAKING ACTION

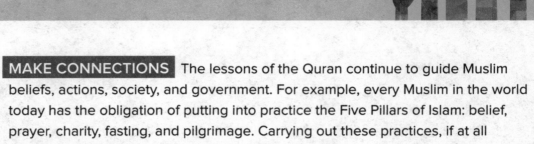

MAKE CONNECTIONS The lessons of the Quran continue to guide Muslim beliefs, actions, society, and government. For example, every Muslim in the world today has the obligation of putting into practice the Five Pillars of Islam: belief, prayer, charity, fasting, and pilgrimage. Carrying out these practices, if at all possible, provides a framework for each Muslim's life.

DIRECTIONS: Think about life in the United States. What are the beliefs and practices that provide a framework and foundation for American life? Look to America's founding documents, such as the Declaration of Independence and the Constitution, for ideas. Think about the customs and routines of your life, your school, and your community. Then write and give a speech in which you propose a list of pillars of American life.

_____

_____

_____

_____

_____

_____

_____

_____

_____

_____

_____

_____

_____

CHAPTER
4

India in the Middle Ages

ESSENTIAL QUESTION
Why do civilizations rise and fall?

Think about how this question might relate to military conquests, trade, and cultural exchanges in India during this time period.

TALK ABOUT IT COLLABORATE

Discuss with a partner what type of information you would need to know to answer this question. For example, one question might be: What role did military conquests play in empire building?

DIRECTIONS: Now write down three additional questions that would help you explain how conflict, trade, and cultural exchanges influenced the rise of major dynasties and key leaders in India.

MY RESEARCH QUESTIONS

Supporting Question 1:

_____

_____

Supporting Question 2:

_____

_____

Supporting Question 3:

_____

_____

ESSENTIAL QUESTION

Why do civilizations rise and fall?

As you gather evidence to answer the Essential Question, think about:

- how trade networks carried goods and cultural ideas.
- how prosperity in the Gupta Empire influenced life in classical India.

My Notes

_____

_____

_____

_____

_____

_____

_____

_____

_____

_____

_____

Classical Age of India

DIRECTIONS: Search for evidence in Chapter 4, Lesson 1 to help you answer the following questions.

1 ECONOMICS Complete the following chart to record the impact of how the development of trade and trade routes influenced the rise and fall of dynasties in India.

ECONOMIC IMPACT OF TRADE

2A **EXPLAINING CAUSE AND EFFECT** What strategies did early Gupta rulers use to create an empire?

_____

_____

_____

2B **MAKING CONNECTIONS** How did the Gupta rulers unite people across their empire in northern India?

_____

_____

_____

3 GEOGRAPHY How did the geography of the region contribute to the spread of the Gupta Empire?

_____

_____

_____

_____

4 **EXPLAINING CAUSE AND EFFECT** The Gupta period saw a number of important advancements in art, science, and mathematics. In the graph below, identify the impact a key innovation from the Gupta Empire had on later civilizations.

GUPTA INNOVATION	IMPACT ON CIVILIZATIONS
ASTRONOMY: Theory of Earth's rotation and that it revolves around the Sun	
TECHNOLOGY: Crystallized sugar	
MATHEMATICS: Symbols for the numbers 1 to 9	

ESSENTIAL QUESTION
Why do civilizations rise and fall?

A Record of Buddhist Kingdoms

DIRECTIONS: Read the following excerpt and answer the accompanying questions.

EXPLORE THE CONTEXT: The Chinese Monk Faxian embarked on a journey through Central Asia to India between 399 and 414 C.E. He went on this journey to find copies of Buddhists texts and monastic rules. Faxian's writings provide an important firsthand account of Buddhist sites and practices during this time period in northern India. In this excerpt, Faxian has arrived at Pataliputra, the seat of power in the Gupta Empire.

VOCABULARY

vie: compete
benevolence: goodwill
righteousness: decency
procession: parade

king-post: a post in the center of a roof
cubit: unit of measurement
tope: dome-shaped structure
devas: divine beings

PRIMARY SOURCE: TRAVEL RECORD

" The cities and towns of this country are the greatest of all in the Middle Kingdom. The inhabitants are rich and prosperous, and vie with one another in the practice of benevolence and righteousness. Every year on the eighth day of the second month they celebrate a procession of images. They make a four-wheeled car, and on it erect a structure five storeys by means of bamboos tied together. This is supported by a king-post, with poles and lances slanting from it, and is rather more than twenty cubits high, having the shape of a tope. White and silk-like cloth of hair is wrapped all round it, which is then painted in various colours. They make figures of devas, with gold, silver, and lapis lazuli grandly blended and having silken streamers and canopies hung out over them. On the four sides are niches [nooks], with a Buddha seated in each, and a Bodhisattva standing in attendance on him. . . . This is the practice in all the other kingdoms as well. The Heads of Vaisya families in them establish in the cities houses for dispensing [giving out] charity and medicines. All the poor and destitute [needy] in the country, orphans, widowers and childless men, maimed [injured] people and cripples, and all who are diseased, go to those houses, and are provided every kind of help. . . . "

—from *A Record of Buddhist Kingdoms, Being an Account by The Chinese Monk Fâ-hien of his Travels in India and Ceylon* (A.D. 399-414)

1 **DESCRIBING** What materials are used to make the figures of devas?

_____

_____

_____

2 **ANALYZING SOURCES** Examine the way Faxian describes the inhabitants of Pataliputra. Why does he consider the people "rich and prosperous" and engaged in "the practice of benevolence and righteousness?"

_____

_____

_____

_____

3 **ANALYZING SOURCES** Which words did Faxian use to alert his reader that he is describing a special religious ceremony? Underline the words he used.

_____

_____

_____

4 **HISTORY** How does Faxian's description of the city of Pataliputra inform our understanding of daily life in the Gupta Empire?

_____

_____

_____

_____

ESSENTIAL QUESTION

Why do civilizations rise and fall?

VOCABULARY

reeds: grasses

sedge: grass-like plant

wont: customary behavior

calyx: outside leaves of a flower bud

Greek Reports of India

DIRECTIONS: Read the following excerpt and answer the accompanying questions.

EXPLORE THE CONTEXT: Herodotus was an early Greek historian who traveled and described the actions and sights he witnessed. This excerpt from his 430 C.E. account of the Persian Wars gives us an outsider's perspective on how the Western world viewed the people of India.

PRIMARY SOURCE: BOOK

"The tribes of Indians are numerous, and do not all speak the same language—some are wandering tribes, others not. They who dwell in the marshes along the river live on raw fish, which they take in boats made of reeds, each formed out of a single joint. These Indians wear a dress of sedge, which they cut in the river and bruise; afterwards they weave it into mats, and wear it as we wear a breast-plate. . . . There is another set of Indians whose customs are very different. They refuse to put any live animal to death, they sow no corn, and have no dwelling-houses. Vegetables are their only food. There is a plant which grows wild in their country, bearing seed, about the size of millet-seed, in a calyx; their wont is to gather this seed and having boiled it, calyx and all, to use it for food. If one of them is attacked with sickness, he goes forth into the wilderness, and lies down to die; no one has the least concern either for the sick or for the dead."

— Herodotus, *The History of Herodotus, Volume 2*

1 HISTORY What elements of life seem to be important to Herodotus, based on how he describes the people of India?

_____

_____

_____

2 **INFERRING** Herodotus describes the diets of two different peoples of ancient India. What did those Indians eat, and what can you infer from their diets about the people of ancient India?

_____

_____

_____

_____

_____

3 **ANALYZING SOURCES** After referring to the text, describe what you know about the people of India from Herodotus. What cultural elements unify or divide them?

_____

_____

_____

_____

4 **DETERMINING CONTEXT** What factors influenced the descriptions and point of view from which Herodotus presents a portrait of the people in India?

_____

_____

_____

_____

ESSENTIAL QUESTION

Why do civilizations rise and fall?

As you gather evidence to answer the Essential Question, think about:

• the influence of Indian culture and power on other civilizations.

• how religious beliefs in India changed over time.

My Notes

_____

_____

_____

_____

_____

_____

_____

_____

_____

_____

Hinduism and Buddhism

DIRECTIONS: Search for evidence in Chapter 4, Lesson 2 to help you answer the following questions.

1 | HISTORY | Use the chart to identify some changes to Hinduism that came about through the Bhakti movements between the 500s C.E. and the 1500s.

RESULTS OF THE BHAKTI MOVEMENTS

2 **MAKING CONNECTIONS** How does the idea of equality in spiritual matters affect ideas about power?

_____

_____

_____

3 CITING TEXT EVIDENCE Use the chart to describe the impact of religious developments in Hinduism and Buddhism on civilizations inside and outside India.

RELIGIOUS DEVELOPMENTS	IMPACT
Hindu sacred texts, including song and verse, are written in the common language.	
Buddhism divides into Theravada and Mahayana.	
Rulers built large religious temples.	

ESSENTIAL QUESTION

Why do civilizations rise and fall?

VOCABULARY

monastery: home of monks

hewn: cut

stout: sturdy

sanctuary: shelter

quafees: servants of the church

deacons: ministers

stole: scarf or shawl

protruding: jutting

The City of Calicut

DIRECTIONS: Read the following excerpt and answer the accompanying questions.

EXPLORE THE CONTEXT: Vasco da Gama was a Portuguese explorer who set sail for India in 1497. Upon his arrival in the city of Calicut in May 1498, he recorded his impressions of the people and the city. Vasco da Gama believed the Hindu people he encountered were Christians.

PRIMARY SOURCE: DIARY

❝The city of Calicut is inhabited by Christians . . . When we arrived they took us to a large church, and this is what we saw: The body of the church is as large as a monastery, all built of hewn stone and covered with tiles. At the main entrance rises a pillar of bronze as high as a mast, on the top of which was perched a bird . . . In addition to this, there was another pillar as high as a man, and very stout. In the center of the body of the church rose a chapel, all built of hewn stone, with a bronze door sufficiently wide for a man to pass, and stone steps leading up to it. Within this sanctuary stood a small image which they said represented Our Lady. Along the walls, by the main entrance, hung seven small bells. In this church the captain-major said his prayers, and we with him.

We did not go within the chapel, for it is the custom that only certain servants of the church, called quafees, should enter. These quafees wore some threads passing over the left shoulder and under the right arm, in the same manner as our deacons wear the stole. They threw holy water over us, and gave us some white earth, which the Christians of this country are in the habit of putting on their foreheads, breasts, around the neck, and on the forearms. They threw holy water upon the captain-major and gave him some of the earth, which he gave in charge of someone, giving them to understand that he would put it on later. Many other saints were

. . . continued

painted on the walls of the church, wearing crowns. They were painted variously, with teeth protruding an inch from the mouth, and four or five arms. **"**

—from *A Journal of the First Voyage of Vasco da Gama, 1497–1499*

1 ANALYZING SOURCES What construction materials are used within the Hindu temple that Vasco da Gama visits?

_____

_____

_____

2 INFERRING How does Vasco da Gama's description of the temple he visits help a reader understand why he mistook the Hindu place of worship for a Christian church?

_____

_____

_____

_____

3 ANALYZING SOURCES Which words did Vasco da Gama use that best show how he is comparing the customs in this religious building with those he is familiar with? Underline the words he used.

_____

_____

_____

4 HISTORY How does Vasco da Gama's reception by the people in Calicut inform our understanding of this city as a major trade center in the 1400s?

_____

_____

_____

The Buddha at the Ajanta Caves

DIRECTIONS: Examine the following image and answer the accompanying questions.

EXPLORE THE CONTEXT: The photograph below shows a rock-cut sculpture of the Buddha from the Ajanta caves. Thirty caves are carved into the rocky face of a mountain located in northwest India. These caves, a series of monasteries, residences, and sanctuaries, are dedicated to the life of the Buddha and date from 200 B.C.E to 650 C.E.

PRIMARY SOURCE: RELIEF SCULPTURE

1 ANALYZING How is the Buddha depicted in this sculpture? Is he a God or a wise teacher?

_____

_____

_____

2 HISTORY In what ways do you think the history of the rise of the ruling dynasties in northern India influenced the creation of monastic sites, such as the Ajanta caves?

_____

_____

_____

3 ANALYZING SOURCES Refer to the lesson text, and then describe the function of the Ajanta caves.

_____

_____

_____

_____

4 ANALYZING SOURCES Does this representation of the Buddha reflect the Mahayana or Theravada branch of Buddhism?

_____

_____

_____

_____

ESSENTIAL QUESTION

Why do civilizations rise and fall?

As you gather evidence to answer the Essential Question, think about:

- the emergence of Islam in India.
- how art and architecture represented a blending of Hindu and Islamic culture.

My Notes

_____

_____

_____

_____

_____

_____

_____

_____

_____

_____

Islam in India

DIRECTIONS: Search for evidence in Chapter 4, Lesson 3 to help you answer the following questions.

1A **EXPLAINING CAUSE AND EFFECT** Arab and Persian Muslim traders traveled to the west coast of India. How did this affect the spread of Islam in this region?

_____

_____

_____

_____

1B **IDENTIFYING STEPS** How did the fall of the Gupta Empire in the mid-500s leave northern India open to raids and conquest?

_____

_____

_____

_____

2 GEOGRAPHY In which parts of India were the sultans of the Delhi Sultanate able to introduce Islam to the people?

_____

_____

3 HISTORY Use the chart to identify some results that came about from Muslim rule in India.

RESULTS OF MUSLIM RULE IN INDIA

4 **RELATING EVENTS** The blending of Islamic and Indian cultures gave birth to new forms of artistic achievement, architecture, and advances in mathematics. How did this cultural exchange ultimately lead to instability?

_____

_____

_____

_____

ESSENTIAL QUESTION

Why do civilizations rise and fall?

Mughal Art

DIRECTIONS: Read the following excerpt and answer the accompanying questions.

EXPLORE THE CONTEXT: Akbar the Great ruled the Mughal Empire from 1555 to 1605 C.E. Like the other rulers in the Mughal Empire during this time, Akbar was Muslim. In contrast with earlier Muslim rulers, Akbar was tolerant of other religious practices and encouraged philosophical and spiritual debates in search of "ultimate truth." Akbar is credited with embracing the blending of Islamic and Hindu art and architecture. In this excerpt, the scholar Abū al-Faẓl describes Akbar's position on art.

PRIMARY SOURCE: BOOK

❝Bigoted followers of the letter of the law are hostile to the art of painting; but their eyes now see the truth. One day at a private party of friends, His Majesty, who had conferred on several the pleasure of drawing near him, remarked: 'There are many that hate painting; but such men I dislike. It appears to me as if a Painter had quite peculiar means of recognizing God; for a painter in sketching anything that has life, and in devising its limbs, one after the other, must come to feel that he cannot Bestow Individuality upon his work, and is thus forced to think of God, the Giver of life, and will thus increase in knowledge.' The number of master-pieces of painting increased with the encouragement given to the art.❞

— Abū al-Faẓl ibn Mubārak, *The Ain i Akbari, Volume 1*, 1590–1596

VOCABULARY

Bigoted: opinionated
conferred: awarded
devising: planning
Bestow: give

1 **ANALYZING SOURCES** What was the impact of Akbar's support of artistic depictions of God?

_____

_____

_____

_____

2 INFERRING The writer notes that those who follow the "letter of the law" are "hostile to the art of painting." Why might artistic representations of God create hostility in people of the Islamic faith?

_____

_____

_____

_____

_____

3 ANALYZING SOURCES After referring to the text, describe what you know about the way Akbar unified people in India during his rule. Why are his thoughts on painting in this excerpt important?

_____

_____

_____

_____

_____

_____

_____

4 INFERRING How does the author of this excerpt feel about what Akbar has contributed to art?

_____

_____

_____

_____

_____

_____

Monotheism in India

ESSENTIAL QUESTION

Why do civilizations rise and fall?

DIRECTIONS: Read the following excerpt and answer the accompanying questions.

EXPLORE THE CONTEXT: Francis Xavier was a Catholic saint and a Jesuit priest and missionary. He traveled to Goa, India, at the request of the Portuguese king in order to spread Christianity. In this excerpt of a letter dated 1543, Francis Xavier writes to Rome with his observations of the beliefs of the Indian people.

PRIMARY SOURCE: LETTER

❝I have found just one Brahmin and no more in all this coast who is a man of learning: he is said to have studied in a very famous Academy. Knowing this, I took measures to converse with him alone. He then told me at last, as a great secret, that the students of this Academy are at the outset made by their masters to take an oath not to reveal their mysteries, but that, out of friendship for me, he would disclose them to me. One of these mysteries was that there only exists one God, the Creator and Lord of heaven and earth, whom men are bound to worship, for the idols are simply images of devils. The Brahmins have certain books of sacred literature which contain, as they say, the laws of God. The masters teach in a learned tongue, as we do in Latin. He also explained to me these divine precepts one by one; but it would be a long business to write out his commentary, and indeed not worth the trouble. Their sages keep as a feast our Sunday. On this day they repeat at different hours this one prayer: "I adore Thee, O God; and I implore Thy help for ever." They are bound by oath to repeat this prayer frequently, and in a low voice. My friend added, that the law of nature permitted them to have more wives than one, and their sacred books predicted that the time would come when all men should embrace the same religion.❞

— from *The Life and Letters of St. Francis Xavier, Volume 1*

VOCABULARY

converse: talk
outset: beginning
disclose: reveal

learned: educated
precepts: principles
sages: thinkers
implore: beg

1 ANALYZING SOURCES What elements of faith does Francis Xavier consider of primary importance in understanding the people of India?

_____

_____

_____

_____

2 DETERMINING CONTEXT Examine the language that Francis Xavier uses to describe the relationship he has established with the Brahmin. How does this inform your understanding of Francis Xavier's approach to the people he meets in India?

_____

_____

_____

_____

3 ANALYZING SOURCES Which words does Francis Xavier use to describe his opinion of the divine precepts relayed to him? Underline the words he used.

_____

_____

_____

4 HISTORY What does the belief in one God demonstrate about the culture of India during the time of Francis Xavier's mission work?

_____

_____

_____

_____

ESSENTIAL QUESTION

Why do civilizations rise and fall?

1 Think About It

Review the Supporting Questions that you developed at the beginning of the chapter. Review the evidence that you gathered in Chapter 4. Were you able to answer each Supporting Question?

If there was not enough evidence to answer your Supporting Questions, what additional evidence do you think you need?

_____

_____

_____

_____

2 Organize Your Evidence

Use a chart like the one below to organize the evidence you will use to support your position statement.

Central Idea

_____

_____

_____

_____

3 Write About It

A position statement related to the Essential Question should reflect your conclusion about the evidence. Write a position statement for the ESSENTIAL QUESTION: *Why do civilizations rise and fall?*

_____

_____

_____

_____

_____

_____

_____

_____

4 Connect to the Essential Question

On a separate piece of paper, create at least five interview questions as if you were interviewing a person who lived in Calicut in the 1400s. Think about asking why he or she lives in this major trade center, what religion he or she practices, how he or she views traders that arrive into port, etc.

Using the Essential Question as a guide, write an "interview" in which you answer the questions as an inhabitant of Calicut during this period might have.

TAKING ACTION

MAKE CONNECTIONS The heritage of millions of people in the United States includes ancestors from the Indian subcontinent. These Americans are often referred to as South Asians, and they include people whose ancestors came from the modern countries of Bangladesh, Bhutan, India, Nepal, Pakistan, Sri Lanka, and the Maldives. They make up a growing portion of the American population, and you will encounter South Asian Americans in all walks of life. Just as South Asians come from a variety of different countries, these Americans practice a variety of different religions, including Buddhism, Christianity, Hinduism, Jainism, Islam, and Sikhism.

DIRECTIONS: South Asians sometimes face discrimination and even hostility from other Americans, partly because some Americans know very little about the history of people from the Indian subcontinent. Use what you have learned about the people and culture of India in the Middle Ages to write an article for your school newspaper that celebrates the heritage of South Asians. Conclude your article by urging all Americans to embrace this group as a growing and vital part of the American people.

_____

_____

_____

_____

_____

_____

_____

_____

_____

_____

Imperial China

ESSENTIAL QUESTION

How do new ideas change the way people live?

Think about how this question might relate to the way people lived in Imperial China.

TALK ABOUT IT COLLABORATE

Discuss with a partner what type of information you would need to know to answer this question. For example, one question might be: How did Imperial Chinese leaders react to the scientific and cultural progress happening around the world?

DIRECTIONS: Now write down three additional questions that would help you explain how new ideas changed the way of life for the people of Imperial China.

MY RESEARCH QUESTIONS

Supporting Question 1:

_____

_____

Supporting Question 2:

_____

_____

Supporting Question 3:

_____

_____

ESSENTIAL QUESTION

How do new ideas change the way people live?

As you gather evidence to answer the Essential Question, think about:

- how traders and missionaries from other places change the way people think, worship, and live.
- how travel to faraway lands helps influence the way people live.

My Notes

_____

_____

_____

_____

_____

_____

_____

_____

_____

_____

China Reunites

DIRECTIONS: Search for evidence in Chapter 5, Lesson 1 to help you answer the following questions.

1 **IDENTIFYING CAUSE AND EFFECT** Use the cause-and-effect chart to list the factors that led to the major public works of the Sui dynasty, as well as the results of those projects.

Cause	Effect

2 **CONTRASTING** How did the Tang dynasty and the Song dynasty differ?

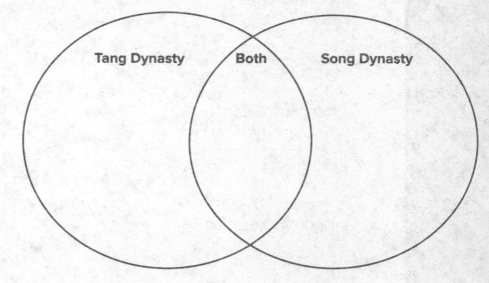

Tang Dynasty   Both   Song Dynasty

3 **ANALYZING** Confucianism and Buddhism both flourished during the Tang and Song dynasties. What evidence from the text helps explain the growth of these belief systems?

_____

_____

_____

_____

_____

_____

_____

_____

_____

4 **IDENTIFYING PERSPECTIVES** Was the return of the civil service exam good or bad? Complete the chart below using information from the text.

Civil Service Exam Pro	Civil Service Exam Con

ESSENTIAL QUESTION

How do new ideas change the way people live?

Tang Dynasty Artifact

DIRECTIONS: Examine the image below and answer the accompanying questions.

EXPLORE THE CONTEXT: The artifact shown in this image comes from the Tang dynasty, which was in power between 600 and 900 C.E. It is made of silver and hammered with a decoration. Its intricate pattern and fine craftsmanship indicate that it was probably an expensive tool used by a successful tradesperson. Trade grew during the rule of the Tang dynasty. The emperors restored the Silk Road, which allowed people to travel to other lands and learn about the way of life in other countries.

PRIMARY SOURCE: ARTIFACT

1. **GEOGRAPHY** What does this artifact tell us about the natural resources available in China during the Tang dynasty?

_____

_____

_____

_____

2. **HISTORICAL CONTEXT** How might the tool in the image be used? What does that tell you about the culture from which it came?

_____

_____

_____

3. **HISTORICAL INFERENCE** What can you infer about the person who designed the tool? How does that help you understand the culture?

_____

_____

_____

_____

4. **DRAWING CONCLUSIONS** What can you conclude about the tool from the fact that it is preserved in a museum?

_____

_____

_____

_____

ESSENTIAL QUESTION

How do new ideas change the way people live?

A Buddhist Bible

DIRECTIONS: Read the passage and answer the accompanying questions.

EXPLORE THE CONTEXT: The translator of the book titled *A Buddhist Bible,* Dwight Goddard, learned about Buddhism when he was 67 years old. He traveled to Asia and collected many texts about the religion, including both primary and secondary sources. He was fascinated by Buddhism and helped bring a greater understanding of it to the United States and elsewhere by translating these works into English.

PRIMARY SOURCE: BOOK EXCERPT

66 Under all circumstances you should free yourselves from attachment to objects; toward them your attitude should be neutral and indifferent. Let neither success nor failure, neither profit nor loss, worry you. Be ever calm and serene, modest and helpful, simple and dispassionate. The Dharma is non-dual as is the mind also. The Path is pure and above all 'form.' You are especially warned not to let the exercise for concentration of mind, fall into mere quiet thinking or into an effort to keep the mind in a blank state. The mind is by nature pure, there is nothing for us to crave or give up. 99

— from *A Buddhist Bible,* Translated in 1932

VOCABULARY

Dharma: the teaching of the Buddha
non-dual: oneness or not separated

1 HISTORY   What type of document is this? How might it have been helpful to the people reading it?

_____

_____

_____

_____

_____

2 **EXPLAINING IDEAS** What instructions does the passage offer as a way of life?

_____

_____

_____

_____

_____

_____

3 HISTORY What was happening in China during the rise of Buddhism that could have made its message especially important to the Chinese people?

_____

_____

_____

_____

_____

_____

_____

_____

4 ECONOMICS The text says that the reader should "free yourselves from attachment to objects." What economic impact would this have for its followers?

_____

_____

_____

_____

_____

_____

_____

ESSENTIAL QUESTION

How do new ideas change the way people live?

As you gather evidence to answer the Essential Question, think about:

- how farm improvements affected the way people lived.
- how artistic expression changed the way people live.

My Notes

_____

_____

_____

_____

_____

_____

_____

_____

_____

_____

Chinese Society

DIRECTIONS: Search for evidence in Chapter 5, Lesson 2 to help you answer the following questions.

1 ECONOMICS Some of the goods produced by Chinese tradespeople were traded all over the world. What were the characteristics of silk and porcelain that made them so economically valuable?

_____

_____

_____

_____

2 **EXPLAINING EFFECTS** Using the graphic organizer below, take notes on the effects of Chinese advancements. Use details from the book to complete the second column.

Advancement	Effect of Advancement
Irrigation Methods	
Coal and Steel	
Printing	
Gunpowder	
Ships	

3 HISTORY The printing press brought an age of literature to China. What did Chinese poetry reveal about the interests of the culture?

_____

_____

_____

_____

_____

_____

_____

_____

_____

_____

_____

_____

4 **ANALYZING** How did the Chinese style of landscape painting reveal the spiritual beliefs of the artists?

_____

_____

_____

_____

_____

_____

_____

_____

_____

_____

_____

_____

Paper Artifact

DIRECTIONS: Study the following image and answer the accompanying questions.

EXPLORE THE CONTEXT: The image shows a playing card from early China's history. It was printed on paper using a woodcut stamp, c. 1400 C.E.

PRIMARY SOURCE: ARTIFACT

1　HISTORY　What type of artifact is this? What does the artifact suggest about the culture in which it was made?

_____

_____

_____

_____

2　**DETERMINING CONTEXT**　What events in China's history help us understand this artifact?

_____

_____

_____

_____

3　**ANALYZING SOURCES**　Look closely at the artifact. What details are important in helping us understand it?

_____

_____

_____

_____

4　**CONNECT TO TODAY**　What do the printed materials we use today tell about our modern culture?

_____

_____

_____

_____

ESSENTIAL QUESTION
How do new ideas change the way people live?

Xuanzang on Life in Magadha

DIRECTIONS: Study the following excerpt and answer the accompanying questions.

EXPLORE THE CONTEXT: Xuanzang [SHEE·AN·ZANG] was born during the Tang dynasty and studied Confucius as a young man. He grew interested in Buddhism and took a 16-year journey to India, traveling along the Silk Road. He wrote about what he learned and the places he saw in his book *Records of the Western Regions of the Great Tang Dynasty*. In this excerpt, he describes Magadha [MAH·guh·dah], a kingdom in northern India where the Buddha spent many years and where he achieved enlightenment.

VOCABULARY

li: the Chinese mile; one *li* measures 1,640 feet

PRIMARY SOURCE: BOOK EXCERPT

❝The country of Magadha is about 5000 li in circuit. The walled cities have but few inhabitants, but the towns are thickly populated. The soil is rich and fertile and the grain cultivation abundant. There is an unusual sort of rice grown here, the grains of which are large and scented and of an exquisite taste. It is specially remarkable for its shining colour. It is commonly called "the rice for the use of the great." As the ground is low and damp, the inhabited towns are built on the high uplands. After the first month of summer and before the second month of autumn, the level country is flooded, and communication can be kept up by boats. The manners of the people are simple and honest. The temperature is pleasantly hot; they esteem very much the pursuit of learning and profoundly respect the religion of Buddha.❞

— Xuanzang, *Records of the Western Regions of the Great Tang Dynasty (Book Six)*, 629 C.E.

1 **DETERMINING CONTEXT** What information does Xuanzang record in his entry about Magadha?

_____

_____

_____

2 **ANALYZING POINTS OF VIEW** How does Xuanzang approach the people and culture of Magadha? What is his point of view about them?

_____

_____

3 **DRAWING CONCLUSIONS** Read Xuanzang's description of the rice product of Magadha. What conclusions can you draw about the author and the culture he is from?

_____

_____

_____

_____

4 HISTORY Based on the description of Magadha, what can you tell about the city in addition to the details that Xuanzang includes? Use evidence from the passage to support your answer.

_____

_____

_____

_____

_____

5 **IDENTIFYING EFFECTS** What effect do you think the details about Magadha would have on Xuanzang's readers after his return to China?

_____

_____

_____

ESSENTIAL QUESTION

How do new ideas change the way people live?

As you gather evidence to answer the Essential Question, think about:

- how the Mongol people affected the culture of China.
- how the strong Mongol leaders brought new ideas to Asia.
- how trade with faraway lands brought new ideas to China.

My Notes

_____

_____

_____

_____

_____

_____

_____

_____

The Mongols in China

DIRECTIONS: Search for evidence in Chapter 5, Lesson 3 to help you answer the following questions.

1 **SEQUENCING** Use the text and the time line organizer below to record how the Mongol Empire grew and changed between 1200 and 1300.

1206:
1227:
1258:
1260:
1279:
1294:

2 ANALYZING ISSUES The Mongols damaged the land they conquered and destroyed many cities and towns. Yet they also brought stability. Analyze whether the Mongols were good or bad for China.

Positive	Negative

3 HISTORY How did the journey of Marco Polo bridge the cultural differences between east and west?

_____

_____

_____

_____

_____

_____

_____

_____

_____

How do new ideas change the way people live?

Artifacts from the Mongols

DIRECTIONS: Study the following image and answer the accompanying questions.

EXPLORE THE CONTEXT: By the mid-1300s, the Mongols ruled a vast empire of the Yuan dynasty. During that time, China reached the height of its wealth and power. The artifacts in this image represent some of the earliest tools that Mongols created from bronze centuries before. They are likely tools that helped people feed themselves.

PRIMARY SOURCE: ARTIFACTS

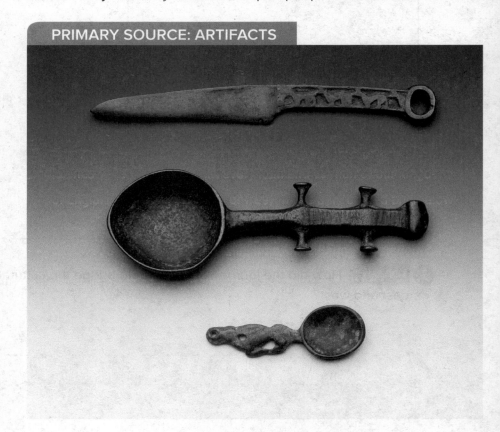

1 **DESCRIBING** Describe the tools shown in the image. Look for detail on the handles.

_____

_____

_____

_____

2 **HISTORICAL INFERENCE** These artifacts were found in China. What can you infer about the area from these artifacts?

_____

_____

_____

_____

3 **HISTORICAL CONTEXT** What do these artifacts tell you about the people who created them?

_____

_____

_____

_____

4 **CONNECT TO TODAY** What instruments or tools from today are similar to the ones in this picture?

_____

_____

_____

_____

ESSENTIAL QUESTION

How do new ideas change the way people live?

Genghis Khan

DIRECTIONS: Study the following passage and answer the accompanying questions.

EXPLORE THE CONTEXT: In the early 1800s, Jacob Abbot wrote a history of Genghis Khan. Abbot is known as an American children's book writer. The history of Genghis Khan is part of the *Makers of History* series.

SECONDARY SOURCE: BOOK EXCERPT

" After the ceremonies of the inauguration were concluded, Genghis Khan returned, with the officers of his court and his immediate followers, to Karakorom. This town, though nominally the capital of the empire, was, after all, quite an insignificant place. . . .

The Monguls and Tartars led almost exclusively a wandering and pastoral life, and all their ideas of wealth and grandeur were associated with great flocks and herds of cattle, and handsome tents, and long trains of wagons loaded with stores of clothing, arms, and other movables, and vast encampments in the neighborhood of rich and extended pasture-grounds. Those who lived permanently in fixed houses they looked down upon as an inferior class, confined to one spot by their poverty or their toil, while they themselves could roam at liberty with their flocks. "

— from *Genghis Khan, Makers of History*, 1901

VOCABULARY

inauguration: the act of placing someone in an official job
nominally: in name only
Tartars: nomadic people of northeastern Mongolia
pastoral: related to grazing sheep or cattle
grandeur: greatness
confined: limited
toil: hard work
roam: wander, travel

1 **ASSESSING CREDIBILITY** Who wrote the passage? What was his occupation and background? How does this information help you understand the document?

_____

_____

_____

_____

_____

2 **COMPARING** What comparison(s) did the author make regarding the way of life of the Mongols?

_____

_____

_____

_____

_____

3 **DRAWING CONCLUSIONS** What can you conclude about the author's view of the Mongols ruled by Genghis Khan?

_____

_____

_____

_____

_____

4 **DESCRIBING** What details are important in understanding the Mongol culture?

_____

_____

_____

_____

_____

ESSENTIAL QUESTION

How do new ideas change the way people live?

As you gather evidence to answer the Essential Question, think about:

- how weak leaders and corruption ended Mongol rule.
- how the Ming dynasty restored peace and security.
- the impact of exploration on the ideas that entered China.

My Notes

_____

_____

_____

_____

_____

_____

_____

_____

_____

The Ming Dynasty

DIRECTIONS: Search for evidence in Chapter 5, Lesson 4 to help you answer the following questions.

1 **ANALYZING** Use the web below to take notes as you read the chapter about the Ming dynasty. Record the ways that the Ming emperors changed how people lived.

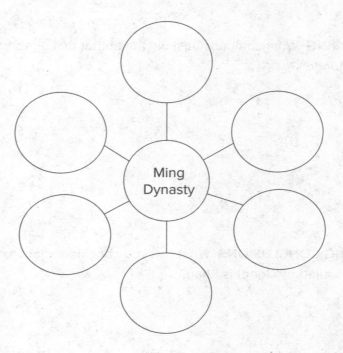

2 **SUMMARIZING** Summarize the details from your textbook to explain how the Ming gradually opened up China to Europeans and outside cultures.

_____

_____

_____

_____

_____

_____

3 RELATING EVENTS Use the chart below to integrate the information in the chapter about Zheng He and his travels.

Who was Zheng He?	
What did he do on his travels?	
When did he travel?	
Where did he go?	
Why did Chinese officials object to the travels?	
How did Zheng He travel?	

The Ming Census

ESSENTIAL QUESTION

How do new ideas change the way people live?

DIRECTIONS: Study the following excerpt and answer the accompanying questions.

EXPLORE THE CONTEXT: The Ming dynasty conducted a census of its subjects in order to help the government collect taxes. The Chinese historian Ping-ti Ho studied that process and the information collected. This passage translates instructions from the Ming Census.

PRIMARY SOURCE: BOOK EXCERPT

❝The officials of the Board of Revenue will take notice that although the country is now at peace the government has not yet secured accurate information about the population . . . The number of persons of each household must all be written down without falsification. Since my powerful troops are no longer going out on campaigns, they are to be sent to every county, in order to make a household-to-household check of the returns. If it is discovered in the course of checking that some local officials have falsified the returns, those officials are to be decapitated. Any common people who hide from the census will be punished according to the law and will be drafted into the army.❞

— Ping-ti Ho, *Studies on the Population of China, 1368–1953*

VOCABULARY

Revenue: income, usually taxes
secured: acquired
falsification: misrepresentation, deception

1 **ANALYZING SOURCES** What type of document is this? How does that help you understand the passage?

_____

_____

_____

_____

_____

_____

2 EXPLAINING What instructions does the emperor give in this passage?

_____

_____

_____

_____

_____

_____

3 CIVICS What aspects of civil society during the Ming dynasty are evident in this passage?

_____

_____

_____

_____

_____

_____

_____

4 DETERMINING CONTEXT What important events were happening at the time this document was created? How does that help us understand the purpose of the document?

_____

_____

_____

_____

_____

_____

*How do new ideas change
the way people live?*

Zheng He's Junks

DIRECTIONS: Study the following image and answer the accompanying questions.

EXPLORE THE CONTEXT: Zheng He's explorations in the early 1400s used about 300 ships and collected many goods, including animals, foods, and drinks foreign to China. These goods were collected on junks, or ships, such as this full-size replica and carried back to China.

PRIMARY SOURCE: ARTIFACT

1 HISTORY Based on its appearance, how do you think this structure was used? Why was it preserved?

_____

_____

_____

_____

2 ECONOMICS What can you tell about the economy of the Ming dynasty from the source?

_____

_____

_____

_____

3 DETERMINING CONTEXT What do you know about the end of Zheng He's expedition that helps you understand this source?

_____

_____

_____

_____

4 INFERRING What inference can you make about the person or people who built this ship?

_____

_____

_____

_____

ESSENTIAL QUESTION

How do new ideas change the way people live?

1 Think About It

Review the supporting questions you developed at the opening of the chapter. Review the evidence you found in Chapter 5. Were you able to answer each of your Supporting Questions?

If you didn't find enough evidence to answer your Supporting Questions, what do you think you need to consider?

_____

_____

_____

_____

2 Organize Your Evidence

Use a web like the one below to organize the evidence you will use to support your position statement.

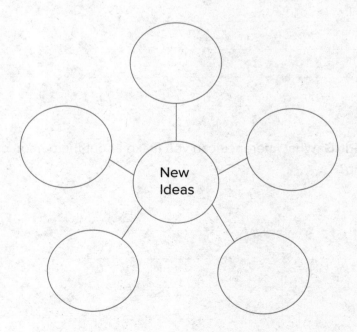

❸ Talk About It

Discuss the evidence you have gathered with a small group or partner. Check your group's understanding of how ideas change the way people live, and answer any questions members may have. Consider any additional advice or input they may have.

❹ Connect to the Essential Question

On a separate piece of paper, choose one invention or idea that emerged from early Chinese culture. Write a magazine article about how that invention or idea influenced the way people lived. Your article should give one example of how the ESSENTIAL QUESTION might be answered: *How do new ideas change the way people live?*

TAKING ACTION

MAKE CONNECTIONS At several points throughout Chinese history, emperors recruited workers to government jobs through a civil service exam. Young men (women were excluded from these jobs) would study for many years for the exam. They would memorize the works of Confucius and work closely with tutors to prepare for the test, which was designed to be very difficult. Just one out of five students passed it. Those who did pass were on a path to a comfortable and prestigious career helping to run the government. Those who failed might be able to work as a clerk or in a small office.

DIRECTIONS: Suppose that government jobs in the United States were the most prestigious jobs available. Consider what kind of test might be used to decide whether a person should be offered a government job. Work with a group of classmates to create an outline and four sample questions for an American civil service test that could be used today. Use what you know about the ideas that change the way people live to help you decide on the topics for the test. Would you test on math? History? Geography? Reading interpretation? Writing ability? Ethics? Combine the questions from every student in your class into a single test. Then, as a class, take the test, and decide whether it would result in the strongest civil servants.

_____

_____

_____

_____

_____

_____

_____

The Civilizations of Korea and Japan

ESSENTIAL QUESTION

How do new ideas change the way people live?

Think about how this question might relate to the early civilizations of Korea and Japan. What new ideas came about in government, warfare, and culture? How did these ideas affect people living in these societies?

TALK ABOUT IT  COLLABORATE

Discuss with a partner the type of information you would need to know to answer these questions. For example, one question might be: Do you recall or know any of the new ideas that came about during this time period in Asia?

DIRECTIONS: Now write down three additional questions that you need to answer to be able to explain how new ideas changed the way people lived.

MY RESEARCH QUESTIONS

Supporting Question 1:

_____

_____

Supporting Question 2:

_____

_____

Supporting Question 3:

_____

_____

ESSENTIAL QUESTION

How do new ideas change the way people live?

As you gather evidence to answer the Essential Question, think about:

- ideas from other countries that influenced Korean society.
- how new ideas changed Korean government, religion, system of writing, and culture.

My Notes

_____

_____

_____

_____

_____

_____

_____

_____

Korea: History and Culture

DIRECTIONS: Search for evidence in Chapter 6, Lesson 1 to help you answer the following questions.

1 IDENTIFYING From where did the early Korean kingdoms get their writing system?

_____

_____

2 HISTORY Who did the three early Korean kingdoms model their governments after?

_____

_____

_____

3 GEOGRAPHY Why do you think Korean culture was influenced by both China and Japan?

_____

_____

_____

_____

4 SUMMARIZING Use the graphic organizer below to list ideas that developed in Korea and their origins.

Ideas from Chinese Culture	Ideas Unique to Korea	Ideas from Japanese Culture

5 IDENTIFYING CAUSE AND EFFECT How did Korea transition from three kingdoms to one under the Koryo dynasty?

_____

_____

6 DESCRIBING What new ideas emerged during the Yi dynasty?

_____

_____

_____

_____

7 SUMMARIZING Complete the following chart.

Individual	Contribution to Korean Culture or Government
Wang Kon	
Yi Song-gye	
Sejong	
Yi-sun Shin	

How do new ideas change the way people live?

Statue of the Buddha

DIRECTIONS: Examine the image below and answer the accompanying questions.

EXPLORE THE CONTEXT: This photograph shows a large Buddha statue from the Koryo dynasty c. 900 C.E. Buddhism arrived on the Korean peninsula in the fourth century, about five hundred years before the founding of the Koryo dynasty.

PRIMARY SOURCE: STATUE

1 **IDENTIFYING** What materials were used to make this statue? Why is this significant?

_____

_____

_____

_____

_____

2 **ANALYZING** What do you think is the meaning of the statue's posture?

_____

_____

_____

_____

3 **HISTORY** Who was ruling Korea at the time this statue was built? What can you infer about their policies on religion from this image?

_____

_____

_____

_____

_____

4 **GEOGRAPHY** From where did the ideas represented by this statue come?

_____

_____

_____

_____

5 **DRAWING CONCLUSIONS** What does this statue tell you about how new ideas changed the way Koreans lived?

_____

_____

_____

_____

ESSENTIAL QUESTION

How do new ideas change the way people live?

Chŏng Inji on the Development of the Korean Alphabet

DIRECTIONS: Read the following excerpt and answer the accompanying questions.

EXPLORE THE CONTEXT: One of the greatest kings during the Yi dynasty in Korea was named Sejong. He was interested in scientific research, innovation, and spreading literacy. During his reign, Koreans used thousands of Chinese characters to read and write, so to simplify the writing system, he developed a phonetic alphabet called *hangul*. Chŏng Inji, one of the finest scholars of his day and an adviser to Sejong, wrote the following about the invention of the Korean alphabet.

VOCABULARY

Monarch: king
adduce: offer or put forth
approprieties: qualities that are suitable or proper
reverentially: in a humble and respectful way

proclaim: announce
enact: make to be law
transmit: communicate
isolated: cut off or separate

SECONDARY SOURCE: BOOK

❝In the winter of the year kye-hae (1443–1444), Our Monarch originated and designed the twenty-eight letters of the Correct Sounds, and he adduced in outline examples and approprieties by which to demonstrate them. He named them "The Correct Sounds for the Instruction of the People." . . . We note reverentially that under our Monarch, with his Heaven-loosed wisdom, the codes and measures that have been proclaimed and enacted exceed and excel those of a hundred kings. The making of the correct sounds is not something that has been transmitted by our ancestors; they have been perfected out of nature itself. Now since there is no place where the all-reaching Pattern is not found, this is certainly not a man-made, isolated thing.❞

1 HISTORY What was Chŏng Ing's purpose in writing about the creation of the alphabet?

_____

_____

_____

_____

2 **ANALYZING** How do you think creating a new alphabet helped spread literacy in Korea?

_____

_____

_____

_____

3 **CITING TEXT EVIDENCE** From where does Chŏng Ing believe Sejong come up with the structure for the Korean alphabet? What evidence can you cite from the excerpt?

_____

_____

_____

_____

_____

4 **MAKING CONNECTIONS** If each word in English had its own symbol, how many symbols do you think you would need to learn to be literate?

_____

_____

_____

_____

_____

ESSENTIAL QUESTION

How do new ideas change the way people live?

As you gather evidence to answer the Essential Question, think about:

- the origins of Japan's different systems of government and how they influenced life for the Japanese people.
- how different religions and belief systems, such as Shinto, animism, and Buddhism, changed or flourished under different rulers.

My Notes

_____

_____

_____

_____

_____

_____

_____

_____

_____

_____

_____

_____

Early Japan

DIRECTIONS: Search for evidence in Chapter 6, Lesson 2 to help you answer the following questions.

1 GEOGRAPHY Why did Japan develop a strongly independent civilization?

_____

_____

_____

_____

2 **SUMMARIZING** Complete the table with details about what characterized the following different periods of rule in early Japan.

The Yamato
Prince Shotoku
The Nara Period

3 DESCRIBING From where did early Japanese emperors claim their authority to rule?

_____

_____

_____

4 MAKING CONNECTIONS How does the practice of animism still influence Japanese culture today?

_____

_____

_____

5 CIVICS Why did Prince Shotoku create a constitution? On what did he base his ideas for some of the specific rules of the constitution?

_____

_____

6 DETERMINING CENTRAL IDEAS Fill in the graphic organizer with specific details of the following elements of life in early Japan.

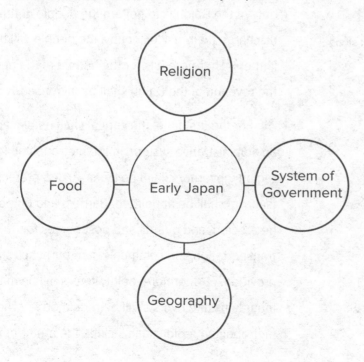

The Reform Edict of Taika

ESSENTIAL QUESTION
How do new ideas change the way people live?

DIRECTIONS: Read the following excerpt and answer the accompanying questions.

EXPLORE THE CONTEXT: Early Japan was divided by clans and ruled by emperors who felt they received the right to rule from heaven. Around 600 C.E., Prince Shotoku created the first constitution. After his death, the ruling Yamato clan enacted the Taika, or Great Change. These changes were decreed in the Reform Edict of Taika. The edict was written by two princes, one who later ruled as Emperor Tenchi. Japan was divided into districts that reported to the emperor and began to pay taxes to government officials. These changes created Japan's first strong, central government.

VOCABULARY

administrative: governing or managing
outpost: military station
allocation: division or sharing out
redistribution: giving out in a new way
alderman: member of a local ruling body
cultivation: farming
prevention: action that stops something
requisition: demand for something

1 SUMMARIZING How did the reform edict change the main structure of Japanese society at the time?

_____

_____

_____

_____

PRIMARY SOURCE: IMPERIAL EDICT

❝I. Let the following be abolished: the titles held by imperial princes to serfs granted by imperial decrees (koshiro); the titles to lands held directly by the imperial court (miyake); and private titles to lands and workers held by ministers and functionaries (omi, muraji and tomo no miyatsuko) of the court, by local nobles (kuni no miyatsuko), and by village chiefs (mura no obito). In lieu thereof, sustenance households shall be granted to those of the rank of Daibu (Chief of a bureau or of a ward) and upwards on a scale corresponding to their positions. Cloth and silk stuffs shall be given to the lower officials and people, varying in value. It is said that the duty of the Daibu is to govern the people. If they discharge their task diligently, the people will have trust in them. Therefore it is for the benefit of the people that the revenue of the Daibu shall be increased.

"II. For the first time, the capital shall be placed under an administrative system. In the metropolitan (or capital) region, governors (kuni no tsukasa) and prefects (kori no tsukasa) shall be appointed. Barriers and outposts shall be erected, and guards and post horses for transportation and communication purposes shall be provided. Furthermore, bell-tokens shall be made and mountains and rivers shall be regulated . . . The metropolitan region shall include the area from the

Yokogawa (river) in Nahari on the east, from (mount) Senoyama in Kii on the south, from Kushibuchi in Akashi on the west, and from (mount) Afusakayama in Sasanami in Omi on the north . . .

"III. It is hereby decreed that household registers, tax registers, and rules for allocation and redistribution of the land shall be established. Each fifty households shall be constituted into a village (ri), and in each village there shall be appointed an alderman. He shall be responsible for the maintenance of the household registers, the assigning of the sowing of crops and the cultivation of mulberry trees, the prevention of offenses, and the requisitioning of taxes and forced labor. All rice-fields shall be measured by a unit called a tan which is thirty paces in length by twelve paces in breadth. Ten tan make one cho. For each tan, the tax (so or denso) shall be two sheaves and two bundles of rice; for each cho, the tax shall be twenty-two sheaves of rice. **"**

— written by Prince Naka-no-ōe and Nakatomi-no Kamatari

2 **DESCRIBING** According to the edict, what was the duty of the Daibu, and how did they increase their earnings?

_____

_____

_____

_____

3 **ANALYZING** Why do you think Emperor Tenchi enacted the Reform of Taika?

_____

_____

_____

4 **CITING TEXT EVIDENCE** If you were a farmer, how would the Reform of Taika change the way you live? What evidence can you cite from the excerpt?

_____

_____

_____

5 **MAKING CONNECTIONS** What do you think were the benefits and drawbacks of having a strong, central government?

_____

_____

_____

6 GEOGRAPHY How did the new central government mark the boundaries of the metropolitan region?

_____

_____

_____

The Kondei System

ESSENTIAL QUESTION

How do new ideas change the way people live?

DIRECTIONS: Read the following excerpt and answer the accompanying questions.

EXPLORE THE CONTENT: In ancient Japan, the central government's military was usually made up of conscripted peasants required to serve as part of a labor obligation to the state. Emperor Kammu, who ruled from 782–806 C.E., questioned the effectiveness of a military made up of unorganized men from the countryside. In 792 Kammu decreed a series of military reforms including the Kondei System, sometimes translated as "stalwart youth," or "able-bodied young men."

PRIMARY SOURCE: IMPERIAL DECLARATION

"An Official Order of the Council of State on the matter relating to the recruitment of the kondei (physically able). Thirty people from the province of Yamato. Thirty people from the province of Kawachi. Twenty people from the province of Izumi.

1. ...Previously [on the seventh day of this month], the Minister of the Right [Fujiwara Tsugunawa] declared that in obedience to the imperial command [all military divisions consisting of] conscript soldiers stationed in the provinces should be abolished with the exception of those in the important border areas. The munitions depots, outposts, and governmental offices which were previously defended by them should be defended by the kondei to be sent to those positions. We now order that you select those physically able from among the sons of the district chiefs (kōri no tsukasa), and place them to serve on these posts on a rotating basis.

Eleventh year of Enryaku (792), sixth month, 14th day. "

VOCABULARY

official: formal, approved by government
council: people running local government

recruitment: enrolling into an army
conscripted: drafted, enlisted
munitions depots: places where arms are stored

1 **COMPARING** What does Emperor Kammu's decree have in common with the Reform Edict of Taika?

_____

_____

_____

_____

2 **ANALYZING** How did the Reform Edict of Taika prepare the way for the Kondei System?

_____

_____

_____

_____

3 **IDENTIFYING** What is a draft? How was it changed by this official order?

_____

_____

_____

_____

_____

4 **MAKING CONNECTIONS** Compare and contrast the system for recruiting soldiers under the Kondei System with the system used in the United States today.

_____

_____

_____

_____

ESSENTIAL QUESTION

How do new ideas change the way people live?

As you gather evidence to answer the Essential Question, think about:

- new ideas in Japanese culture and the different groups who contributed them.
- how Japanese culture is still influenced by beliefs and practices begun during the Medieval period.

My Notes

_____

_____

_____

_____

_____

_____

_____

_____

_____

Medieval Japan

DIRECTIONS: Search for evidence in Chapter 6, Lesson 3 to help you answer the following questions.

1 **SUMMARIZING** What caused Japanese emperors to slowly lose power and influence?

_____

_____

2A **DETERMING THE CENTRAL IDEA** Fill in the graphic organizer with specific details about the samurai.

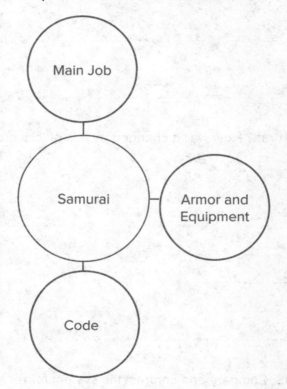

2B **ANALYZING** Why were the shogun created?

_____

_____

3 **ANALYZING** How did the creation of the position of shogun change the central government of Japan?

_____

_____

_____

4 **DESCRIBING** Who benefited the most from Japan's prosperity under the Ashikaga Shogunate?

_____

_____

5 **SUMMARIZING** Use the graphic organizer to list the main products or duties of the following roles in shogunate Japan.

Farmers	Artisans
Women	Writers
Architect Artisans	Creative Artisans

6 **DESCRIBING** How is Shinto different from Buddhism?

ESSENTIAL QUESTION

How do new ideas change the way people live?

Samurai and Daimyo

DIRECTIONS: Examine the image below and answer the accompanying questions.

EXPLORE THE CONTEXT: This photograph shows a man standing, facing right, and a man wearing a sword kneeling before him, facing left, holding another sword as though offering it to the man standing in front of him. It is believed to depict a samurai kneeling before a daimyo around 1877.

PRIMARY SOURCE: PHOTOGRAPH

1 **IDENTIFYING** What was the role of a daimyo?

_____

_____

_____

_____

_____

2 CIVICS What was the likely relationship between the samurai and the daimyo depicted in this photograph? How is this relationship illustrated in the photograph?

_____

_____

_____

_____

_____

_____

3 DESCRIBING How did a samurai's loyalty to his daimyo change the way people lived in Japan?

_____

_____

_____

_____

_____

_____

4 DETERMINING POINT OF VIEW What do you think the photographer was trying to show by taking the picture of these two men in this position?

_____

_____

_____

_____

_____

_____

ESSENTIAL QUESTION
How do new ideas change the way people live?

Hojo Shigetoki's Letter of Instruction to His Son Nagatoki

DIRECTIONS: Read the excerpt below and answer the accompanying questions.

EXPLORE THE CONTEXT: Hojo Shigetoki was a leading samurai in Japan. In 1247, the Kamakura shoguns appointed his 18-year-old son to a key position. Shigetoki then wrote his son a letter instructing him in the ways of the warrior.

VOCABULARY

subordinates: those of lower rank
obvious: easy to see
distinction: difference
misdeeds: errors
circumstances: situations
provocation: baiting
haste: speed
remorse: regret, sorrow

PRIMARY SOURCE: LETTER

"... In dealing with subordinates do not make an obvious distinction between good and not-good. Use the same kind of language, give the same kind of treatment to all, and thus you will get the best out of the worst. But you yourself must not lose sight of the distinction between good character and bad character, between capable and incapable. You must be fair, but in practice you must not forget the difference between men who are useful and men who are not. Remember that the key to discipline is fair treatment in rewards and in punishments. But make allowances for minor misdeeds in young soldiers and others, if their conduct is usually good . . . Remember, however, that there are times when a commander must exercise his power of deciding questions of life or death. In those circumstances since human life is at stake you must give most careful thought to your action. Never kill or wound a man in anger, however great the provocation. Better get somebody else to administer the proper punishment. Decisions made in haste before your feelings are calm can only lead to remorse. Close your eyes and reflect carefully when you have a difficult decision to make. When accusations are brought to you, always remember that there must be another side to the question. Do not merely indulge in anger. To give fair decisions is the most important thing not only in commanding soldiers but also in governing a country. "

1 HISTORY How does this letter demonstrate aspects of the code of Bushido?

_____

_____

_____

_____

_____

_____

2 ANALYZING What was Shigetoki's purpose in writing this letter? What do you think he meant by the phrase, "thus you will get the best out of the worst"?

_____

_____

_____

_____

_____

_____

3 MAKING CONNECTIONS If your own parent or guardian were to write you a letter, what do you think they would say? What kind of a code do you think they would want you to live by?

_____

_____

_____

_____

_____

_____

ESSENTIAL QUESTION

How do new ideas change the way people live?

❶ Think About It

Review the Supporting Questions that you developed at the beginning of the chapter. Review the evidence that you gathered in Chapter 6. Were you able to answer each Supporting Question?

If there was not enough evidence to answer your Supporting Questions, what additional evidence do you think you need to consider?

_____

_____

_____

_____

❷ Organize Your Evidence

Use a chart like the one below to organize the evidence you will use to support your position statement.

New Idea	Origin of the Idea	Influence on Korean or Japanese Civilization	Source of information to cite as evidence	How evidence helps support my position statement

3 Write About It

A position statement related to the Essential Question should reflect your conclusion about the evidence. Write a position statement for the ESSENTIAL QUESTION: *How do new ideas change the way people live?*

_____

_____

_____

_____

_____

_____

_____

4 Talk About It

Work in a small group to present your position statement and evidence. Gather feedback from your classmates before you write your final conclusion. You may choose to refine your position statement after you have discussed it with your classmates. Group members should listen to one another's arguments, ask questions, and offer constructive advice about the statement.

5 Connect to the Essential Question

On a separate piece of paper, develop a written interview to answer the ESSENTIAL QUESTION: *How do new ideas change the way people live?* Choose one new idea that you learned about in this chapter and write an interview as if you were able to speak with someone who was involved in implementing the new idea. Through your interview, readers should be able to understand the idea and how it changed a specific society.

CITIZENSHIP
TAKING ACTION

MAKE CONNECTIONS New ideas often spread from culture to culture. Research some currently popular songs from Korea or Japan. Do you see influences from other cultures in the song or does the song influence other cultures?

DIRECTIONS Popular music is often used to express people's feelings about their government and culture and encourage people to take action. Choose an issue related to the chapter, such as styles of governance, warfare, class hierarchy, or geographical influence, and write your own song lyrics on that issue. Volunteers may wish to perform their songs for the class.

_____

_____

_____

_____

_____

_____

_____

_____

_____

_____

_____

_____

_____

_____

The Americas

ESSENTIAL QUESTION
What makes a culture unique?

Think about how this question might relate to natural resources and the rise and fall of early civilizations in the Americas.

TALK ABOUT IT COLLABORATE

Discuss with a partner what type of information you would need to know to answer this question. For example, one question might be: How did the natural world and competition for resources influence the daily lives and sacred beliefs of the early civilizations in the Americas?

DIRECTIONS: Now write down three additional questions that would help you explain how the natural world influenced the development of cultures and civilizations in the Americas.

MY RESEARCH QUESTIONS

Supporting Question 1:

_____

_____

Supporting Question 2:

_____

_____

Supporting Question 3:

_____

_____

ESSENTIAL QUESTION

What makes a culture unique?

As you gather evidence to answer the Essential Question, think about:

- how the early American cultures shifted from hunter-gathering to farming.
- the link between sacred beliefs and farming in the civilizations of Mesoamerica.

My Notes

_____

_____

_____

_____

_____

_____

_____

_____

_____

_____

The First Americans

DIRECTIONS: Search for evidence in Chapter 7, Lesson 1 to help you answer the following questions.

1A EXPLAINING CAUSE AND EFFECT How did the shift from hunting and gathering to farming relocate where unique civilizations thrived in Mesoamerica?

_____

_____

_____

1B GEOGRAPHY What role did sacred beliefs play in the lives of the first Americans?

_____

_____

_____

_____

2 GEOGRAPHY How did the landscape of Mesoamerica influence the rise and fall of different civilizations?

_____

_____

_____

3 **EXPLAINING CAUSE AND EFFECT** Fill in the chart below to describe how elements of the natural world impacted culture in the Americas.

Natural Elements	Impact on Culture
Weather	
Geography	
Animals	

4 ECONOMICS Use the chart below to record the ways that competition for resources impacted Mesoamerican civilizations.

Effects of Competition for Resources

ANALYZE THE SOURCE

ESSENTIAL QUESTION

What makes a culture unique?

An Olmec Figurine

DIRECTIONS: Analyze the artifact below and answer the accompanying questions.

EXPLORE THE CONTEXT: The Olmec were the earliest civilization to thrive in Mesoamerica near the Gulf of Mexico from c. 2700 B.C.E. to 900 B.C.E. Known for the colossal heads they carved from basalt with detailed faces of their rulers, the Olmec also created small figurines using basalt, jade, terracotta, and wooden materials. The image of the figurine below shows an example of the Olmec artistic tradition in sculpture. Figurines have been found at a variety of locations, including in everyday households and at burial sites. The subjects of these smaller figurines were often representations of Olmec Gods, like the "Rain Baby." They also include examples of people engaged in activities, such as playing a traditional Olmec ballgame. This ballgame was an important sport in the Olmec culture. It also had religious significance and became a feature of later cultures, including the Maya and the Aztec. Many elements of Mesoamerican art, including sculpture and ceramic traditions, can be traced back to the Olmec.

PRIMARY SOURCE: ARTIFACT

1 **DESCRIBING** Describe the figurine and the material you think might have been used to create it. How do you think this figurine was used by the Olmec people?

_____

_____

2 **ANALYZING** Why do you think Olmec figurines have been found at both common household sites and burial sites? Explain your answer.

_____

_____

_____

3 **ANALYZING SOURCES** Does your analysis agree with the lesson text's description of what types of images were depicted in Olmec figurines and statues?

_____

_____

_____

4 **HISTORY** How do you think the art of the Olmec represented their culture and impacted later civilizations?

_____

_____

_____

_____

ESSENTIAL QUESTION

What makes a culture unique?

The Aztec Calendar

DIRECTIONS: Examine the following image and answer the accompanying questions.

EXPLORE THE CONTEXT: This image shows an Aztec calendar. Many elements of the Aztec culture, including the development of a calendar system, can be traced back to earlier civilizations in the Mesoamerican region, including the Maya. The Aztec calendar is a wheel with two distinct cycles. The first is a 365-day cycle that was based on the sun and used for agriculture. The second is a 260-day cycle that was used for religious rituals. Together, these cycles made up a 52-year unit of time similar to our century. In the center of the wheel is the representation of the sun God. In the next circle are 20 symbols for periods of time that are 13 days in length. The Aztec believed each 13-day period belonged to a different God and balance had to be maintained between each God in order for the people to thrive.

PRIMARY SOURCE: ARTIFACT

1 **DESCRIBING** Do you recognize any of the figures depicted in the images on this calendar? Why do you think these images were used on this calendar?

_____

_____

_____

_____

2 HISTORY How did the development of Aztec culture influence the development of this calendar?

_____

_____

_____

_____

3 **ANALYZING SOURCES** Review the text and the image, and then describe what you know about the importance of the Aztec's sacred days.

_____

_____

_____

_____

4 **DRAWING CONCLUSIONS** How do you think the natural world influenced the development of this calendar?

_____

_____

_____

_____

_____

_____

ESSENTIAL QUESTION

What makes a culture unique?

As you gather evidence to answer the Essential Question, think about:

- the importance of agriculture to civilizations in the Americas.
- how culture in the Americas evolved and was reflected in daily life and activities.

My Notes

_____

_____

_____

_____

_____

_____

_____

_____

_____

Life in the Americas

DIRECTIONS: Search for evidence in Chapter 7, Lesson 2 to help you answer the following questions.

1 HISTORY Use the chart to identify the impact of agriculture on early American civilizations and culture.

> IMPACT OF AGRICULTURE

> Rise of Complex Societies

> Sacred Practices and Beliefs

> Innovation

> Competition and War

2 **EXPLAINING IDEAS** Consider how the farming practices of the Maya were linked to their culture. What role did corn play in their sacred beliefs?

_____

_____

3 **CITING TEXT EVIDENCE** Use the chart to give examples of projects the Inca began in order to improve Inca society.

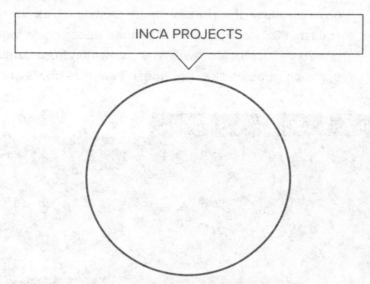

INCA PROJECTS

4 **SUMMARIZING** Use the chart to identify where each of the groups listed lived.

North American Peoples	
Inuit	
Tlingit	
Haida	
Chinook	
Chumash	
Pomo	
Zuni	

ESSENTIAL QUESTION

What makes a culture unique?

Nazca Pottery

DIRECTIONS: Examine the following image and answer the accompanying questions.

EXPLORE THE CONTEXT: This bowl is an example of Nazca pottery from the Andean region of present-day Peru. Early people in this region hunted animals and fished along the coast. Farming efforts in the inland region proved difficult due to dry, desert-like conditions. The Nazca created underground irrigation canals that enabled them to grow a variety of important staple crops such as corn, beans, and squash. Many of the colorful, painted decorations found on Nazca pottery reflect their growth as a civilization from farming. Rulers and common people alike used these ceramics bowls and vessels.

PRIMARY SOURCE: ARTIFACT

1 **ANALYZING** What do you think this piece of pottery was used for, based on its shape, size, and decoration?

_____

_____

_____

2 **DRAWING CONCLUSIONS** What does the decoration tell you about the Nazca?

_____

_____

_____

_____

_____

3 **COMPARING** Compare the text information describing the Nazca pottery with this image. How does the image support what is said in the text?

_____

_____

_____

_____

4 **HISTORY** In what ways do you think the ability of the Nazca to create pottery reflects a complex society?

_____

_____

_____

_____

A Conqueror's View of the Inca

DIRECTIONS: Read the following excerpt and answer the accompanying questions.

EXPLORE THE CONTEXT: Pedro de Cieza de Léon was a Spanish conquistador who interviewed native people in the Andean region of what is now Peru. This excerpt gives us a view into the Inca system of record keeping and governance.

PRIMARY SOURCE: FIRST-HAND ACCOUNT

"[I]n the time of the Kings Incas, orders were given through all the towns and provinces of Peru, that the principal lords and their lieutenants should take note, each year, of the men and women who had died, and also of the births. For as well for the assessment of tribute, as for calculating the number of men that could be called upon to serve as soldiers, and for the defence of the villages such information was needed. This was easily done, because each province, at the end of the year, was ordered to set down in the quipus, by means of the knots, all the men who had died in it during the year, as well as all who were born. In the beginning of the following year, the quipus were taken to Cuzco, where an account was made of the births and deaths throughout the empire. These returns were prepared with great care and accuracy, and without any fraud or deceit. When the returns had been made up, the lord and his officers knew what people were poor, the number of widows, whether they were able to pay tribute, how many men could be taken for soldiers and many other facts which were considered, among these people, to be of great importance. As this empire was of

VOCABULARY

quipu: the Inca system of counting by placing knots on lengths of rope or colored thread

Cuzco: a city situated in the Andean mountains of modern Peru that served as the center of the Inca Empire

fraud: deception
deceit: dishonesty
extent: size
allies: individuals associated by a common goal or purpose
provisions: supplies of food and resources

1 **CITE TEXT EVIDENCE** What was the purpose of collecting information about the total number of births and deaths in each province and region?

_____

_____

_____

_____

_____

_____

such vast extent, . . . there were a great number of storehouses for provisions and other necessaries for a campaign, and for the equipment of soldiers, if there was a war these great resources were used where the camps were formed, without touching the supplies of allies, or drawing upon the stores of different villages. If there was no war, all the great store of provisions was divided amongst the poor and the widows. **"**

—Pedro de Cieza de Léon, *The Second Part of the Chronicle of Peru,* 1540

2 **DETERMINING MEANING** Examine how excess provisions were used by the Inca. How is the distribution of this resource important to understanding their culture?

_____

_____

_____

_____

_____

3 **CITING TEXT EVIDENCE** Which passage from Pedro de Cieza de Léon's account describes the Inca Empire as relying on a strong, central government? Underline the words he used.

_____

_____

_____

_____

4 HISTORY How does Pedro de Cieza de Léon's point of view affect the way that he describes the Inca system?

_____

_____

_____

_____

_____

_____

_____

ESSENTIAL QUESTION

What makes a culture unique?

① Think About It

Review the Supporting Questions that you developed at the beginning of the chapter. Review the evidence that you gathered in Chapter 7. Were you able to answer each Supporting Question?

If there was not enough evidence to answer your Supporting Questions, what additional evidence do you think you need?

_____

_____

_____

_____

② Organize Your Evidence

Use a chart like the one below to organize the evidence you will use to support your position statement. You could also create a Web diagram with your position statement in the center and supporting evidence in the surrounding ovals.

central and supporting ideas

3 Write About It

A position statement related to the Essential Question should reflect your conclusion about the evidence. Write a position statement for the ESSENTIAL QUESTION: *What makes a culture unique?*

_____

_____

_____

_____

_____

_____

_____

_____

_____

4 Connect to the Essential Question

On a separate piece of paper, create at least five good questions you would use if you were Pedro de Cieza de Léon interviewing someone who lived in the Inca Empire prior to the arrival of the Spanish. Questions might include why he or she settled where they did, what the advantages and disadvantages were, how he or she needed to adapt to the environment, or other similar questions.

Using the Essential Question as a guide, write an "interview" in which you answer the questions as an early Inca might have.

CITIZENSHIP
TAKING ACTION

MAKE CONNECTIONS Think about the ways that natural resources affect your home, family, and community. What are the ways that the use and conservation of natural resources affects the way you live?

DIRECTIONS: Students take a cultural issue in their community and collaborate in order to provide solutions to the issue and promote the solutions via social media.

_____

_____

_____

_____

_____

_____

_____

_____

_____

_____

_____

_____

_____

_____

_____

CHAPTER 8

African Civilizations

ESSENTIAL QUESTION
Why do people trade?

Think about how this question might relate to the cultural exchanges between African civilizations and other parts of the world during this time period.

COLLABORATE

TALK ABOUT IT

Discuss with a partner what type of information you would need to know to answer this question. For example, one question might be: How did the establishment of trade routes across the Sahara and Sahel regions impact African society?

DIRECTIONS: Now write down three additional questions that would help you explain how trade developed among African civilizations, as well as between Africa and other parts of the world.

MY RESEARCH QUESTIONS

Supporting Question 1:

_____

_____

Supporting Question 2:

_____

_____

Supporting Question 3:

_____

_____

ESSENTIAL QUESTION

Why do people trade?

As you gather evidence to answer the Essential Question, think about:

- the role of geography in the rise of civilizations.
- how trade encouraged cultural exchange.

My Notes

The Rise of African Civilizations

DIRECTIONS: Search for evidence in Chapter 8, Lesson 1 to help you answer the following questions.

1A IDENTIFYING CAUSE AND EFFECT What elements of the landscape impacted where civilizations developed in Africa?

_____

_____

_____

_____

_____

_____

_____

1B How did the Sahara and Sahel zones impact cultural exchange between East and West Africa?

_____

_____

_____

_____

2 GEOGRAPHY Why was the Niger River important to the rise of civilizations in West Africa?

_____

_____

_____

_____

3 **IDENTIFYING CAUSE AND EFFECT** The participation of West African civilizations in the Africa-Europe-Asia trade network between 400 B.C.E. and 1400 C.E. greatly impacted these societies. In the graphic below, identify why the following elements of trade were so important to the West African kingdoms.

ELEMENT OF TRADE	VALUE
CAMELS	
SALT	
GOLD	

4 ECONOMICS Complete the following chart to record the impact of how the development of trade and trade routes influenced the West African kingdoms.

Economic Impact of Trade

Equestrian Figure from the Mali Empire

DIRECTIONS: Examine the following image and answer the accompanying questions.

EXPLORE THE CONTEXT: The image below is a terra-cotta sculpture, created between 1200 and 1400 C.E. and found near the city of Djenne. This city became an important stop in the trans-Sahara trade route. The Mali warrior is depicted dressed in military gear and astride a horse. Some Arabic documents note that Mansa Musa had a cavalry of more than 100,000 during his reign in the early 1300s C.E. Horses were not native animals to Africa and required tremendous care and maintenance.

PRIMARY SOURCE: SCULPTURE

1 **ANALYZING** What do the warrior and horse appear dressed to do in this sculpture?

_____

_____

_____

_____

2 **HISTORY** How might the history of the rise of the Mali Empire be illustrated in this sculpture?

_____

_____

_____

3 **ANALYZING TEXT EVIDENCE** After referring to the text, describe the significance of this warrior being depicted on horseback.

_____

_____

_____

_____

_____

4 **DRAWING CONCLUSIONS** What important clues does this statue provide about the Mali Empire?

_____

_____

_____

ESSENTIAL QUESTION

Why do people trade?

The West African Griot

DIRECTIONS: Read the following excerpt and answer the accompanying questions.

EXPLORE THE CONTEXT: Griots served an important role in the royal courts of West African rulers. These artists were storytellers who relayed the history of the empires to the people.

> ## PRIMARY SOURCE: BOOK
>
> ❝ The bard, or griot, in West Africa, who used to relate the epic, was first and foremost an artist. His aim was to entertain the listeners who were fond of hearing about the prowess and exploits of the kings and warriors. The griot usually accentuated the superhuman dimensions of the hero. In order to make his tale more pleasant, he skillfully used his art, the literary form of his narrative, the beauty of this language and any other device which could strike the imagination of his listeners. He emphasized decisive moments such as fights, provocations, plots and magical scenes. . . . in order to make his narrative enjoyable, the griot was usually accompanied by a musical instrument. Indeed, in West Africa, the strong rhythm of the epic was almost always punctuated by a ngoni, a khalam, or a tam-tam, and the crowd participated by repeating the refrain in chorus. ❞
>
> —from *An Introduction to the African Prose Narrative,* 2004

VOCABULARY

prowess: skill, talent
exploits: heroic acts, adventures
accentuated: highlighted

decisive: significant
provocations: causes of anger

1 **CITING TEXT EVIDENCE** What was the goal of most griots?

_____

_____

_____

2 DETERMINING MEANING What can you determine about the meaning of the words "ngoni, a khalam, or a tam-tam" based on this context?

_____

_____

_____

_____

_____

3 ANALYZING TEXT EVIDENCE After referring to the text, describe what you know about the people of West Africa based on the role of the griot in this society. Think about the elements that unified the culture.

_____

_____

_____

_____

_____

_____

_____

_____

4 DRAWING CONCLUSIONS What point of view does this historian use when describing the griot?

_____

_____

_____

_____

_____

_____

ESSENTIAL QUESTION

Why do people trade?

As you gather evidence to answer the Essential Question, think about:

- the role of trade in the spread of Islam in Africa.

- the influence of Islam on African society and government.

My Notes

_____

_____

_____

_____

_____

_____

_____

_____

Africa's Governments and Religions

DIRECTIONS: Search for evidence in Chapter 8, Lesson 2 to help you answer the following questions.

1 **INTERPRETING** Why did some West African leaders originally accept Islam?

_____

_____

_____

_____

_____

2 **CITING TEXT EVIDENCE** Use the chart to describe how the elements of adopting Islam in African civilizations impacted their society.

ADOPTION OF ISLAM	IMPACT
Trade with Muslim merchants and civilizations	
Adoption of Islamic laws	
Teaching the Quran	

3 **HISTORY** Use the chart to identify some results that sprang from the introduction of Islam to the kingdoms in Africa.

RESULTS OF THE INTRODUCTION OF ISLAM TO AFRICAN KINGDOMS

ESSENTIAL QUESTION
Why do people trade?

West African Military and Trade

DIRECTIONS: Read the following excerpt and answer the accompanying questions.

EXPLORE THE CONTEXT: The historian John Powell describes the importance of the trans-Saharan trade route as a source of wealth. African rulers taxed the goods being traded and also raised funds by offering protection to travelers along trade routes.

SECONDARY SOURCE: BOOK

❝Ghana's emergence as the first of the West African empires ultimately set the stage for subsequent developments identified with the establishment of the kingdoms of Mali and Songhai. In each instance the intensification of trade along the trans-Saharan trade network was a critical factor underlying the expansion, influence and institutionalization of the military orders of the day. In fact, much of the wealth generated to support the maintenance of professional armies—documented by various Islamic writers to have ranged between 40,000 and 200,000 soldiers—was derived directly from the military and police protections afforded foreign travelers merchants on the trans-Saharan trade corridor.❞

— John Powell, *Weapons & Warfare: Modern Weapons and Warfare (since c. 1500)*, 2010

VOCABULARY

ultimately: finally
subsequent: later
intensification: building up, strengthening

institutionalization: to establish as usual, or normal
derived: developed

1 **CITING TEXT EVIDENCE** According to John Powell, how did West African armies pay for their large armies?

_____

_____

_____

_____

_____

2 **DETERMINING MEANING** What does Powell's description of the military tell you about the structure of West African governments?

_____

_____

_____

_____

_____

_____

_____

_____

_____

_____

3 **CITING TEXT EVIDENCE** Which phrase does Powell use to describe the relationship between trade and the size of the military? Underline the words he used.

_____

_____

_____

_____

_____

_____

4 HISTORY How does this perspective on African government influence our understanding of how trade impacted West African life?

_____

_____

_____

_____

_____

_____

ESSENTIAL QUESTION
Why do people trade?

Rituals and Beliefs of the Nyakyusa

DIRECTIONS: Read the following excerpt and answer the accompanying questions.

EXPLORE THE CONTEXT: The Nyakyusa were a Bantu-speaking people who lived in the area north of Tanzania, in the Ngonde plain. Monica Wilson records the rituals and beliefs of this people in the following excerpt focused on the ruler called King Kyungu.

SECONDARY SOURCE: ANTHROPOLOGICAL STUDY

"Great precautions were taken to preserve his health. He lived in a separate house with his powerful medicines . . . When the Kyungu did fall ill he was smothered by the nobles who lived around him at Mbande, and buried in great secrecy, with a score or more of living persons—slaves—in the grave beneath him, and one or two wives and the sons of commoners above. And in the midst of all this slaughter the nobles brought a sheep to look into the grave that the dead Kyungu might be gentle (mololo) like the sheep! The living Kyungu was thought to create food and rain, and his breath and the growing parts of his body—his hair and nails and the constantly replaced mucus of his nose—were believed to be magically connected with the fertility of the Ngonde plain. When he was killed his nostrils were stopped so that he was buried 'with the breath in his body'; while portions of his hair and nails and of his nasal mucus were taken from him beforehand and buried by the nobles of Ngonde in the black mud near the river. This was 'to defend the country against hunger, to close up the land, to keep it rich and heavy and fertile as it was when he himself lived in it.' "

— Monica Wilson, *Communal Rituals of the Nyakyusa*, 1970

VOCABULARY

precautions: safety measures
nasal: having to do with the nose
beforehand: in advance

1 **ANALYZING** What is one of the primary roles of the Kyungu as described in this excerpt?

_____

_____

_____

_____

2 **HISTORY** What does the role of the Kyungu illustrate about the Bantu people's relationship with their environment?

_____

_____

_____

_____

_____

3 **ANALYZING TEXT EVIDENCE** After referring to the text, describe what you know about the practices and beliefs of the Nyakyusa.

_____

_____

_____

_____

_____

4 **DRAWING CONCLUSIONS** What can you determine about the Nyakyusa beliefs by examining how they treat the Kyungu when he falls ill?

_____

_____

_____

_____

_____

ESSENTIAL QUESTION

Why do people trade?

As you gather evidence to answer the Essential Question, think about:

- the cultural traditions and ideas that many African societies share.
- the reasons for the origination of slavery in Africa.

My Notes

_____

_____

_____

_____

_____

_____

_____

_____

_____

_____

_____

African Society and Culture

DIRECTIONS: Search for evidence in Chapter 8, Lesson 3 to help you answer the following questions.

1A **IDENTIFYING CAUSE AND EFFECT** How did Bantu people spread their beliefs and ideas to large portions of Africa?

_____

_____

_____

_____

1B What role did families play in African society?

_____

_____

_____

_____

_____

_____

2 **GEOGRAPHY** How did geography determine which regions were most impacted by the Atlantic slave trade?

_____

_____

_____

_____

_____

_____

_____

_____

3 HISTORY Use the chart to identify some cultural results of the family serving as the central unit of African society.

CULTURAL RESULTS OF AFRICAN SOCIETY BASED ON FAMILY

4 INTERPRETING How did the capture and forced removal of enslaved people impact African societies?

_____

_____

_____

_____

_____

ESSENTIAL QUESTION

Why do people trade?

African Folktales

DIRECTIONS: Read the following excerpt and answer the accompanying questions.

EXPLORE THE CONTEXT: The Bantu people, a term that includes a large variety of ethnic groups, have common mythology and folklore. The following is typical of Bantu narratives that feature talking animals that are symbolic of different human attributes. These were most often used to educate the listener.

VOCABULARY

ingrained: deep-rooted

tortoise: a land-dwelling turtle

lot: sort

self-coloured: being of a single color

makora: Swahili word for "scamp" or "rascal"

domesticate: tame

PRIMARY SOURCE: FOLKTALE

"The hyena, for no apparent reason beyond ingrained ill-nature, put the tortoise up into the fork of a tree, where he could not get down. A leopard passed by and saw him: "Do you also climb trees, Tortoise?" "The hyena is the person who put me there, and now I can't get down if I try." The leopard remarked, "Hyena is a bad lot," and took the tortoise out of the tree. We are not told what the leopard looked like at this time, but he would seem to have been 'self-coloured,' for the tortoise, offering out of gratitude for his rescue to "make him beautiful, did so by painting him with spots, saying, as he worked, "Where your neighbour is all right, be you also all right [*makora*]." The leopard, when he went off, met a zebra, who admired him so much that he wanted to know who had made him beautiful, and himself went to the tortoise. In this way he got his stripes. This "Just-so" story accounts not only for the markings of the leopard and the zebra, but for their being creatures of the wild, for when the people, hoeing their gardens, saw them they exclaimed, "Oh! the big beauty! Catch it and let us domesticate it!" or words to that effect, so both of them fled into the bush, where they have remained ever since."

—"How the Leopard Got His Spots" from *Myths and Legends of the Bantu* [Date unknown]

1 **CITING TEXT EVIDENCE** How is the hyena portrayed here?

_____

_____

_____

2 **DETERMINING MEANING** What is the significance of this narrative and the belief, "Where your neighbour is all right, be you also all right?"

_____

_____

_____

_____

_____

_____

_____

3 **ANALYZING TEXT EVIDENCE** After referring to the text, what do you know about the Bantu people? Why is a story featuring animals important to understanding this civilization?

_____

_____

_____

_____

_____

_____

_____

4 **DRAWING CONCLUSIONS** What can you determine about the Bantu culture based on this folktale?

_____

_____

_____

ESSENTIAL QUESTION
Why do people trade?

West African Money Cowries

DIRECTIONS: Read the following excerpt and answer the accompanying questions.

EXPLORE THE CONTEXT: Cowries functioned in African societies as currency, jewelry, and religious accessories. These shells symbolized strength, fertility, and wealth. Cowrie shells played an important role in the Atlantic trade of enslaved people, as well. Cowrie shell artifacts have been discovered in old enslaved peoples' quarters that were dug up for study in the United States.

SECONDARY SOURCE: BOOK

" In sub-Saharan West Africa, cowries were the most popular currency for centuries. These so-called "money cowries" are the shells of small snail-like creatures that live in the tropical waters of the Indian and Pacific Oceans. As early as the 13th century, Arab traders were carrying cowries from the Maldive Islands in the Indian Ocean to Egypt, then across the desert to the markets of sub-Saharan West Africa. Europeans were interested to find that in commercial transactions, Africans tended to prefer cowries to gold, and by the 16th century the shells were being imported in the ships of Dutch and English traders to the Guinea coast of West Africa. "

—from *Empires of Medieval West Africa: Ghana, Mali, and Songhay,* 2005

VOCABULARY

currency: money
*commercial
transactions:* business
dealings

advent: beginning

① **CITING TEXT EVIDENCE** What role did cowries play in Atlantic trade?

_____

_____

_____

_____

_____

2 DETERMINING POINT OF VIEW What perspective does this author give on the value of cowries compared to gold in West African society?

_____

_____

_____

_____

_____

_____

3 CITING TEXT EVIDENCE Which words serve as a clue to understanding why cowries might be so highly valued by West Africans? Underline the words, and explain why this is the best clue.

_____

_____

_____

_____

_____

_____

_____

_____

_____

4 DRAWING CONCLUSIONS: Why do you think cowries were a good form of currency?

_____

_____

_____

_____

_____

_____

_____

ESSENTIAL QUESTION

Why do people trade?

1 Think About It

Review the Supporting Questions that you developed at the beginning of the chapter. Review the evidence that you gathered in Chapter 8. Were you able to answer each Supporting Question?

If there was not enough evidence to answer your Supporting Questions, what additional evidence do you think you need?

_____

_____

_____

_____

2 Organize Your Evidence

Use the chart below to organize the evidence you will use to support your position statement.

Central Idea

Supporting Details

3 Write About It

A position statement related to the Essential Question should reflect your conclusion about the evidence. Write a position statement for the ESSENTIAL QUESTION: *Why do people trade?*

_____

_____

_____

_____

_____

_____

_____

_____

_____

4 Connect to the Essential Question

On a separate piece of paper, write a play about a trade caravan crossing the Saharan desert in the 1300s. Think about describing how the traders will make the journey, what goods they might be carrying, what religion they might practice, how long the journey will take, and what risks are involved.

Keep in mind the Essential Question about why people trade as you write about this journey.

CITIZENSHIP
TAKING ACTION

MAKE CONNECTIONS In this chapter, we have explored a folktale from Africa and what that story reveals about beliefs and cultural traditions. Folktales can be found around the world. In the United States, each region has different sets of folktales and fables that reflect the ethnic background and beliefs of the groups that initially settled these places. In some instances, these ideas no longer reflect the ideas and beliefs of the people.

DIRECTIONS: Research a folktale from the region where you live. Write an article for the school newspaper about what the folktale reveals about the beliefs and practices of the people who settled your region. Be sure and comment on how these beliefs and cultural traditions are similar to and different from those in your community today.

_____

_____

_____

_____

_____

_____

_____

_____

_____

_____

_____

World Religions

ESSENTIAL QUESTION
How do religions develop?

Think about how this question might relate to the religious movements of Protestantism, Sufism, Shia Islam, and Sikhs around the world between 1300 and 1750.

TALK ABOUT IT 🤝 COLLABORATE

Discuss with a partner what type of information you would need to know to answer this question. For example, one question might be: What role did Catholicism play in the development of Protestantism?

DIRECTIONS: Now write down three additional questions that would help you explain how different religious movements emerged, how they gained followers and power, and how these developments influenced governments and the balance of political power.

MY RESEARCH QUESTIONS

Supporting Question 1:

_____

_____

Supporting Question 2:

_____

_____

Supporting Question 3:

_____

_____

ESSENTIAL QUESTION

How do religions develop?

As you gather evidence to answer the
Essential Question, think about:

- how criticism of the Catholic
  Church inspired the Reformation.
- the political implications of the
  Protestant Reformation in Europe.

My Notes

_____

_____

_____

_____

_____

_____

_____

_____

_____

A Reformation in Christianity

DIRECTIONS: Search for evidence in Chapter 9, Lesson 1 to help you
answer the following questions.

1A **IDENTIFYING CAUSE AND EFFECT** What were the criticisms of
the Catholic Church at the time of the Reformation?

_____

_____

_____

_____

_____

_____

1B How had respect for the leaders of the Catholic Church, including
the pope, weakened over time?

_____

_____

_____

_____

2 **GEOGRAPHY** How did location impact the divide between
Protestants and Catholics in Germany?

_____

_____

_____

_____

3 **IDENTIFYING CAUSE AND EFFECT** As the ideas of the Reformation gained popularity and spread across Europe, these ideas influenced the way that people thought about government. In the graphic below, identify the political influence of certain religious ideas.

IDEAS OF THE REFORMATION	IDEAS ABOUT GOVERNMENT
THE ELECTION OF CLERGY	
OBEDIENCE TO THE CHURCH	
PAYING INDULGENCES	

4 ECONOMICS Complete the following chart to record the impact of rulers who decided to embrace Protestant Christianity.

ECONOMIC IMPACT OF REFORMATION

ESSENTIAL QUESTION

How do religions develop?

Criticism of the Catholic Church

DIRECTIONS: Read the following excerpt and answer the accompanying questions.

EXPLORE THE CONTEXT: Desiderius Erasmus was a priest, humanist, and dedicated scholar who found himself caught between the Church and the spirit of the Reformation. A prolific writer, Erasmus wrote to people at all levels within the Church, including the following letter to the Bishop of Augsburg, in Germany.

PRIMARY SOURCE: DIARY

66 The state of the Church distracts me. My own conscience is easy; I was alone in saying from the first that the disorder must be encountered in its germs; I was too true a prophet; the play, which opened with universal hand clapping, is ending as I foresaw that it must. The kings are fighting among themselves for objects of their own. The monks instead of looking for a reign of Christ, want only to reign themselves. The theologians curse Luther and in cursing him curse the truth delivered by Christ and the Apostles and . . . alienate with their foul speeches many who would have returned to the Church or but for them would have never left it. No fact is plainer than that this tempest has been sent from heaven by God's anger, as the frogs and locusts and the rest were sent on the Egyptians; but no one remembers his own faults, and each blames the other. It is easy to see who sowed the seed and who ripened the crop. 99

—Erasmus to the Bishop of Augsburg, August 26, 1528 in *Life and Letters of Erasmus: Lectures Delivered at Oxford 1893-4*

VOCABULARY

encountered: come across; met with
universal: worldwide

theologians: people who study God and religion
alienate: turn away

1 **CITING TEXT EVIDENCE** How does Erasmus describe the theologians' response to Martin Luther's ideas?

_____

_____

_____

_____

2 **DETERMINING MEANING** Examine the language that Erasmus uses to describe the conflict between the Church and the ideas of Martin Luther. What can you determine about his concern for the future based on this context?

_____

_____

_____

_____

_____

3 **ANALYZING TEXT EVIDENCE** After referring to the text, describe how ideas of the Reformation related to power in the government and in the Church.

_____

_____

_____

_____

4 **DRAWING CONCLUSIONS** What is Erasmus's point of view about the Reformation and the Church's response to it?

_____

_____

_____

_____

ESSENTIAL QUESTION
How do religions develop?

The German Peasant Rebellion

DIRECTIONS: Read the following excerpt and answer the accompanying questions.

EXPLORE THE CONTEXT: The German Peasants' Rebellion was a series of uprisings among German-speaking people in Central Europe between 1524 and 1525. Their demands were listed in a document entitled "The Twelve Articles." Some of these demands were inspired by ideas of the Reformation.

PRIMARY SOURCE: PETITION

" The First Article. First, it is our humble petition and desire, as also our will and resolution, that in the future we should have power and authority so that each community should choose and appoint a pastor, and that we should have the right to depose him should he conduct himself improperly. The pastor thus chosen should teach us the gospel pure and simple, without any addition, doctrine, or ordinance of man. "

—from "The Twelve Articles," Demands from the German Peasants, 1524

VOCABULARY

petition: request
depose: remove from office

doctrine: set of guidelines
ordinance: rule

1 **CITING TEXT EVIDENCE** According to this except, what change do the people want in how their religious leaders are appointed?

_____

_____

_____

_____

_____

2 **DETERMINING MEANING** What does the phrase, "The pastor thus chosen should teach us the gospel pure and simple, without any addition, doctrine, or ordinance of man" refer to?

_____

_____

_____

_____

3 **CITING TEXT EVIDENCE** Which words best show the desire of the people to appoint their own religious leaders? Underline the words that best demonstrate what is demanded.

_____

_____

_____

_____

_____

4 **DRAWING CONCLUSIONS** What can you determine about the importance of selecting religious leaders based on where it appears in "The Twelve Demands"?

_____

_____

_____

_____

_____

ESSENTIAL QUESTION

How do religions develop?

As you gather evidence to answer the Essential Question, think about:

- how the Catholic Church attempted reform.
- why the Edict of Nantes was important.

My Notes

_____

_____

_____

_____

_____

_____

_____

_____

Catholics And Protestants

DIRECTIONS: Search for evidence in Chapter 9, Lesson 2 to help you answer the following questions.

1 HISTORY Use the chart to identify some results that sprang from the conflict between Catholics and Protestants.

RESULTS OF CONFLICT BETWEEN CATHOLICS AND PROTESTANTS

2 **INTERPRETING** Consider how religious conflict was more likely in certain geographic regions and countries.

_____

_____

_____

3 **CITING TEXT EVIDENCE** The Thirty Years' War was a period of violent religious conflict. Use the chart to describe the impact of the conflict on the strength of the major empires in Europe.

EMPIRE	IMPACT
France	
Spain	
Holy Roman	

4 **DESCRIBING** How did the role of women change after the end of the Reformation?

_____

_____

_____

_____

_____

_____

Criticism of the Pope

DIRECTIONS: Read the following excerpt and answer the accompanying questions.

EXPLORE THE CONTEXT: Raimon de Cornet was a French priest, troubadour, and poet who opposed the clergy and the pope.

PRIMARY SOURCE: POEM

❝I see the pope his sacred trust betray,

For while the rich his grace can gain alway,

His favors from the poor are aye withholden.

He strives to gather wealth as best he may,

Forcing Christ's people blindly to obey,

So that he may repose in garments golden.

The vilest traffickers in souls are all

His chapmen, and for gold a prebend's stall

He'll sell them, or an abbacy or miter.

And to us he sends clowns and tramps who crawl

Vending his pardon briefs from cot to hall—

Letters and pardons worthy of the writer,

Which leaves our pokes, if not our souls, the lighter.❞

—Raimon de Cornet, c. 1324–1340

VOCABULARY

prebend: payment to the clergy
abbacy: office of abbot or abbess in the Church
miter: bishop's hat

1 CITING TEXT EVIDENCE What are the criticisms of the pope in this poem?

_____

_____

_____

_____

2 DETERMINING MEANING How does the description of indulgences in this poem reinforce the ideas the writer is trying to communicate?

_____

_____

_____

_____

_____

_____

_____

_____

3 CITING TEXT EVIDENCE Which words does the author use to convey his ideas about the corruption that the pope has spread to the clergy? Underline the words he used.

_____

_____

_____

4 HISTORY How does this perspective inform our understanding of the religious conflicts in France during this time?

_____

_____

_____

_____

_____

ESSENTIAL QUESTION
How do religions develop?

A Huguenot on St. Bartholomew's Day

DIRECTIONS: Examine the following image and answer the accompanying questions.

EXPLORE THE CONTEXT: The painting by Sir John Everett Millais in 1852 depicts a couple embracing on St. Bartholomew's Day in 1572 when Catholics in Paris massacred Protestants. The woman in this painting is attempting to tie a white scarf around the arm of her beloved. The white scarf was a marker of Catholicism and would have shielded the man from the massacre. The man is refusing this protection. He is a Huguenot, a French protestant persecuted by the Catholic Church leaders for their faith. The moment in this painting symbolizes the choice between physical safety and spiritual devotion.

SECONDARY SOURCE: PAINTING

1 **ANALYZING** Describe the figures and the setting in this painting.

_____
_____
_____
_____
_____

2 HISTORY This painting dates from 1851, but it depicts an event in France from 1572. In what ways does this inform your understanding of the impact of the religious wars during this time period?

_____
_____
_____
_____
_____

3 **ANALYZING TEXT EVIDENCE** After referring to the text, describe what you know about the significance of the white scarf around the man's arm.

_____
_____
_____
_____
_____

4 **DRAWING CONCLUSIONS** What important statement is the artist making in this painting making about an individual's responsibility to their ideas?

_____
_____
_____
_____

ESSENTIAL QUESTION

How do religions develop?

As you gather evidence to answer the Essential Question, think about:

- how Sufi missionaries spread Islam.
- how the conflict between Shia and Sunni Muslims increased during Safavid rule.

My Notes

Islam and Safavid Persia

DIRECTIONS: Search for evidence in Chapter 9, Lesson 3 to help you answer the following questions.

1A IDENTIFYING CAUSE AND EFFECT How did the conflict between Sunni and Shia Muslims begin?

_____

_____

_____

1B DESCRIBING How did Safavid rule deepen the conflict between the Sunni and Shia branches of Islam in Persia and the Ottoman Empire?

_____

_____

_____

_____

_____

2 GEOGRAPHY How did expansion of the Safavid Empire increase tensions between the Sunnis and Shias?

_____

_____

_____

_____

3 HISTORY Use the chart to identify some results of Sufism.

RESULTS OF SUFISM

[blank box]

[blank box]

[blank box]

[blank box]

4 INTERPRETING Why were Sufi missionaries successful in converting people to Islam?

_____

_____

_____

_____

ESSENTIAL QUESTION
How do religions develop?

VOCABULARY

prevailed: won out

infidels: nonbelievers

jinn: Islamic magic spirit

The Plague in Cairo

DIRECTIONS: Read the following excerpt and answer the accompanying questions.

EXPLORE THE CONTEXT: By the 1200s, Cairo became the largest city in the Muslim world and was an important center of trade and culture. The following excerpt from historian Joseph Patrick Byrne provides a lens to understand the impact of the bubonic plague on this region during the height of the outbreak between 1348 and 1349. It is estimated that up to one-third of the population in Cairo died from the plague.

SECONDARY SOURCE: BOOK

❝Cairo was a Muslim city, and Islamic doctrines on the Plague and proper responses prevailed. Muhammad had taught that the Plague was entirely the will of Allah: it is a mercy to the faithful victims, since they will go immediately to Paradise, and punishment for the infidels. Muslims were to neither flee nor enter a place where the Plague raged; but there was no contagion since God struck down only who he willed. . . . Some considered even prayer for relief to be a faithless act. . . . Ibn Al-Khatib dismissed the jinn and embraced contagion, finding that other rational people did as well . . . people did flee, including the sultan and his entourage who left the Citadel in September 1348. ❞

—from *The Black Death*, 2004

1 **CITING TEXT EVIDENCE** What was the initial response of Islamic leaders to the threat posed by the plague?

_____

_____

_____

2 **DETERMINING MEANING** What is the significance of prayer for relief being considered a faithless act?

_____

_____

_____

_____

_____

_____

3 **ANALYZING TEXT EVIDENCE** After referring to the text, what do you know about the impact of the plague in Cairo, and why is it significant that the sultan left the Citadel?

_____

_____

_____

_____

_____

_____

_____

4 **DRAWING CONCLUSIONS** Based on this evidence, what can you determine about how the plague spread across Asia, the Middle East, and Europe during this period?

_____

_____

_____

_____

_____

_____

Safavid Soldiers

EXPLORE THE CONTEXT: The Safavid Empire relied on a strong military force to conquer new territory and put down internal uprisings. The painting below, c. 1600, shows how these elite Persian soldiers were equipped.

PRIMARY SOURCE: PAINTING

1 **DESCRIBING** How is the soldier in this illustration equipped? What weapons does he possess, and how is he dressed?

_____

_____

_____

_____

2 HISTORY In what ways does this depiction of a Safavid solider reflect the success and wealth of the empire?

_____

_____

_____

_____

_____

3 **ANALYZING TEXT EVIDENCE** After referring to the text, describe what you know about the importance of the Safavid soldier to the empire.

_____

_____

_____

_____

_____

_____

_____

4 **DRAWING CONCLUSIONS** Based on your understanding of the importance of the military to the Safavid Empire, how would a soldier be viewed in the community?

_____

_____

_____

_____

_____

_____

ESSENTIAL QUESTION

How do religions develop?

As you gather evidence to answer the Essential Question, think about:

- the guiding principles in the creation of Sikhism.
- the persecution that adherents to Sikhism faced.

My Notes

_____

_____

_____

_____

_____

_____

_____

_____

_____

_____

_____

Religious Change in South Asia

DIRECTIONS: Search for evidence in Chapter 9, Lesson 4 to help you answer the following questions.

1 HISTORY Use the chart to identify the beliefs that were taught by Guru Nanak and that formed Sikhism.

TEACHINGS OF GURU NANAK

[ ]

[ ]

[ ]

[ ]

2 INTERPRETING Consider how Guru Nanak's ideas challenged the authority of some priests and social abuses of the *jati* system.

_____

_____

_____

_____

3 CITING TEXT EVIDENCE Use the chart below to describe the symbolic meaning of some of the items the Kakar Sikhs are expected to wear after their initiation.

SIKH KHALSA	
KAKAR	SYMBOLISM
Kara: Metal bracelet	
Kirpan: Religious article resembling a knife	
Kanga: Wooden comb	

4 DESCRIBING What was the succession of human Gurus following Guru Nanak? How did it end?

_____

_____

_____

_____

_____

_____

ESSENTIAL QUESTION

How do religions develop?

Guru Gobind Singh

DIRECTIONS: Examine the following image and answer the accompanying questions.

INTRODUCTION: This painting, created in the 1830s, depicts Guru Gobind Singh with fellow Sikhs. Guru Gobind Singh helped shape Sikhism by naming the holy book as his successor.

SECONDARY SOURCE: PAINTING

1 ANALYZING How would you describe Guru Gobind Singh as depicted in this painting?

_____

_____

_____

_____

2 **DRAWING CONCLUSIONS** What does the Guru Gobind Singh's position in the painting tell you about his position in Sikh society?

_____

_____

_____

_____

_____

_____

3 **ANALYZING TEXT EVIDENCE** After referring to the text, describe what you know about the significance of Guru Gobind Singh to Sikhism.

_____

_____

_____

_____

_____

_____

_____

_____

4 HISTORY In what ways do you think the scene depicted in this painting is important to understanding the Sikhs?

_____

_____

_____

_____

_____

_____

Conquering the Sikh Army

DIRECTIONS: Read the following excerpt and answer the accompanying questions.

EXPLORE THE CONTEXT: The following excerpt is from Mirza Mohammad Harisi. He describes the arrival of the defeated Sikh leader Banda Singh and his army into the city of Delhi in February 1716.

VOCABULARY

dejection: sadness
humiliation: shame

PRIMARY SOURCE: BOOK

❝Such a crowd in the bazars and lanes had rarely been seen. The Muslims could hardly contain themselves for joy. But the unfortunate Sikhs, who had been reduced to this condition, were quite happy and contented with their lot. Not the slightest sign of dejection or humiliation was visible on their faces. In fact, most of them, as they passed along on their camels, seemed to be happy and cheerful, merrily singing their sacred hymns. If anyone from the lane called out to them that their own excesses had brought them where they were, they quickly retorted that it had been so decreed by the Almighty, and that their capture and misfortune was in accordance with His will. And if anyone said, 'Now you will be killed,' they shouted, 'Do kill us. When were we afraid of death? Had we been afraid, how could we have fought so many battles with you? It was merely through starvation that we fell into your hands, otherwise, you know already what deeds we are capable of.'❞

—from *A Short History of the Sikhs, Volume One (1469–1765)*

1 **CITING TEXT EVIDENCE** How does the author describe the attitude of the defeated Sikh army?

_____

_____

2 **DETERMINING MEANING** Examine how the author describes the Sikhs. What is his view of the manner in which they enter the city?

_____

_____

_____

_____

_____

_____

_____

3 **CITING TEXT EVIDENCE** Which passage from this account of the Sikhs' arrival into Delhi describes the Sikhs' faith? Underline the words.

_____

_____

_____

_____

_____

_____

4 **HISTORY** How does this account of the capture of Banda Singh and his army help illustrate the persecution that the Sikhs faced?

_____

_____

_____

_____

_____

_____

ESSENTIAL QUESTION

How do religions develop?

1 Think About It

Review the Supporting Questions that you developed at the beginning of the chapter. Review the evidence that you gathered in Chapter 9. Were you able to answer each Supporting Question?

If there was not enough evidence to answer your Supporting Questions, what additional evidence do you think you need?

_____

_____

_____

_____

2 Organize Your Evidence

Use the chart below to organize the evidence you will use to support your position statement.

Central Idea

Supporting Details

③ Write About It

A position statement related to the Essential Question should reflect your conclusion about the evidence. Write a position statement for the ESSENTIAL QUESTION: *How do religions develop?*

_____

_____

_____

_____

_____

_____

_____

_____

_____

④ Connect to the Essential Question

On a separate piece of paper or using a computer, create a graphic that explains the factors that contribute to how religions develop. The graphic should combine visual and textual elements and reflect the evidence you have collected about the development of the different religions discussed in this chapter.

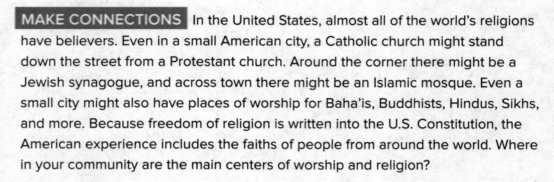

CITIZENSHIP
TAKING ACTION

MAKE CONNECTIONS In the United States, almost all of the world's religions have believers. Even in a small American city, a Catholic church might stand down the street from a Protestant church. Around the corner there might be a Jewish synagogue, and across town there might be an Islamic mosque. Even a small city might also have places of worship for Baha'is, Buddhists, Hindus, Sikhs, and more. Because freedom of religion is written into the U.S. Constitution, the American experience includes the faiths of people from around the world. Where in your community are the main centers of worship and religion?

DIRECTIONS: Work in small groups to make a list of as many different places of worship as you can find in your community. You might use an Internet search engine to help in making this list. Then use what you've found to create a public service announcement (PSA) about the diversity of religion in your community. In your group's PSA, inform the public about the community's diverse religious institutions and also make a plea for tolerance of all the different faiths.

_____

_____

_____

_____

_____

_____

_____

_____

New Ideas

ESSENTIAL QUESTION
How do new ideas change the way people live?

Think about how this question might relate to the Renaissance, the Scientific Revolution, and the Enlightenment.

TALK ABOUT IT COLLABORATE

Discuss with a partner what type of information you would need to know to answer this question. For example, one question might be: Why are the events and ideas that occurred during these eras so significant?

DIRECTIONS: Now write down three additional questions that you need to answer to be able to explain the importance of these eras and their ideas.

MY RESEARCH QUESTIONS

Supporting Question 1:

_____

_____

Supporting Question 2:

_____

_____

_____

Supporting Question 3:

_____

ESSENTIAL QUESTION

How do new ideas change the way people live?

As you gather evidence to answer the Essential Question, think about:

- how secular ideas changed European society.
- the importance of trade to the Italian city-states.
- how exploration led to new ideas and behavior.
- why certain individuals had significant influence in Italy and over the changes that occurred.
- the art, architecture, and writing that developed during these eras.

My Notes

_____

_____

_____

_____

_____

_____

_____

The Renaissance Begins

DIRECTIONS: Search for evidence in Chapter 10, Lesson 1 to help you answer the following questions.

1 **EXPLAINING** How did the shift to a more secular way of life influence the Renaissance?

_____

_____

_____

_____

_____

2 **IDENTIFYING EFFECTS** In the graphic organizer below, describe how each characteristic of Italy influenced the Renaissance.

Characteristic of Italy	Influence on the Renaissance
Italian cities were wealthy.	
Italy was the heart of the old Roman Empire.	
Many Italians lived in cities instead of in rural areas.	
Stronger economies developed.	

3 ECONOMICS   Why were the Italian states able to remain independent and prosper during the Middle Ages?

_____

_____

_____

4 GEOGRAPHY   How did Italy's location affect it during the Renaissance?

_____

_____

_____

_____

5 CIVICS   Complete the chart.

Individual	How He Changed Italian Society and Ideas During the Renaissance
Marco Polo	
Lorenzo de' Medici	
Niccolò Machiavelli	

ESSENTIAL QUESTION
How do new ideas change the way people live?

Niccoló Machiavelli on How to Gain a Ruler's Favor

DIRECTIONS: Read the following excerpt and answer the accompanying questions.

EXPLORE THE CONTEXT: Lorenzo de' Medici was one of the most influential people in Italy's history. Rather than governing Italy as an all-powerful ruler, de' Medici surrounded himself with others who could assist him in his governance. Niccolò Machiavelli dedicated his political treatise on power, *The Prince*, to de' Medici's grandson and ruler at the time, Lorenzo di Piero de' Medici.

PRIMARY SOURCE: BOOK

❝Those who wish to acquire favor with a ruler most often approach him with those among their possessions that are most valuable in their eyes, or that they are confident will give him pleasure. So rulers are often given horses, armor, cloth of gold, precious stones, and similar ornaments that are thought worthy of their social eminence. Since I want to offer myself to your Magnificence, along with something that will symbolize my desire to give you obedient service, I have found nothing among my possessions that I value more, or would put a higher price upon, than an understanding of the deeds of great men, acquired through a lengthy experience of contemporary politics and through an uninterrupted study of the classics. Since I have long thought about and studied the question of what makes for greatness, and have now summarized my conclusions on the subject in a little book, it is this I send your Magnificence. ❞

— Niccoló Machiavelli, *The Prince*, 1513

VOCABULARY

favor: approval, support

eminence: importance, reputation

symbolize: represent

contemporary: modern-day

the classics: classic literature

summarized: to give a short report on a subject

1 CIVICS Why does Machiavelli refer to Lorenzo di Peiro de' Medici as "your Magnificence?"

_____

_____

_____

_____

2 ANALYZING What is the purpose of Machiavelli's letter?

_____

_____

_____

_____

3A IDENTIFYING What does Machiavelli offer de' Medici?

_____

_____

_____

_____

_____

3B ANALYZING Why does Machiavelli offer this in place of "horses, armor, cloth of gold, precious stones, and similar ornaments?"

_____

_____

_____

_____

_____

Lorenzo De' Medici on How a Cardinal Should Live

DIRECTIONS: Read the following excerpt and answer the accompanying questions.

EXPLORE THE CONTEXT: Due to the high-ranking position of the de' Medici family, Lorenzo de' Medici's nephew, Giovanni, became a cardinal in the Roman Catholic Church when he was only 13 years old. The letter below is from Lorenzo to Giovanni after his nephew became a cardinal.

VOCABULARY

retine: servants, attendants
residence: home
endeavor: try, attempt
station: level in society

acquisition: gaining
antiquity: ancient times
learned: educated

PRIMARY SOURCE: LETTER

❝ A handsome house and a well-ordered family will be preferable to a great retinue and a splendid residence. Endeavor to live with regularity, and gradually bring your expenses within those bounds which in a new establishment cannot perhaps be expected. Silk and jewels are not suitable for persons in your station. Your taste will be better shown in the acquisition of a few elegant remains of antiquity, or in the collecting of handsome books, and by your attendants being learned and well-bred rather than numerous. ❞

— Letter from Lorenzo de' Medici to Giovanni de' Medici, 1491

1A IDENTIFYING What is the purpose of Lorenzo's letter?

_____

_____

_____

_____

_____

1B **DESCRIBING** What is Lorenzo's opinion about the acquisition of possessions?

_____

_____

_____

_____

2 `CIVICS` Why does Lorenzo write that "Silk and jewels are not suitable for persons in your station"?

_____

_____

_____

_____

3 **EXPLAINING** Explain why Lorenzo believes that his nephew's "taste will be better shown in the acquisition of a few elegant remains of antiquity, or in the collecting of handsome books, and by your attendants being learned and well-bred rather than numerous."

_____

_____

_____

_____

4 **DETERMINING CONTEXT** Why might it have been important for Giovanni to follow his uncle's advice?

_____

_____

_____

_____

ESSENTIAL QUESTION

How do new ideas change the way people live?

As you gather evidence to answer the Essential Question, think about:

- how new technology helped to spread ideas.
- the significant art and literature that came from the Renaissance.
- how other countries were affected by the changes occurring in Italy.

My Notes

_____

_____

_____

_____

_____

_____

_____

_____

NEW IDEAS AND ART

DIRECTIONS: Search for evidence in Chapter 10, Lesson 2 to help you answer the following questions.

1A **EXPLAINING** What is humanism?

_____

_____

_____

_____

1B **CITING TEXT EVIDENCE** What role did humanism play in the Renaissance?

_____

_____

_____

_____

_____

2 **UNDERSTANDING CHRONOLOGY** Complete the graphic organizer below to explain how Francesco Petrarch contributed to the Renaissance.

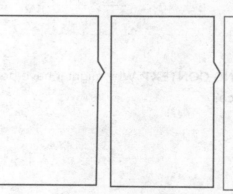

Francesco Petrarch travels to old monasteries.

3 IDENTIFYING EFFECTS The graphic organizer below includes names of individuals who were important to the Renaissance. Identify where each person was born, list a significant contribution made by each individual, and explain how that contribution influenced the Renaissance.

Individual	Country of Origin	Contribution to the Renaissance	How This Contribution Influenced the Renaissance
Dante Alighieri			
Geoffrey Chaucer			
Johannes Gutenberg			
Giotto			

4 GEOGRAPHY How did Italy's location help to expand the art of the Renaissance?

_____

_____

_____

_____

_____

ESSENTIAL QUESTION

How do new ideas change the way people live?

Giotto's *The Lamentation*

DIRECTIONS: Study the image and answer the accompanying questions.

EXPLORE THE CONTEXT: This painting by Giotto is entitled *The Lamentation*, or *Mourning of Christ*. It was painted between 1305 and 1306. In it, the deceased body of Jesus, referred to as "Christ" in the title, is surrounded by various people. Included are figures significant to the Roman Catholic Church, such as Mary Magdalene and John, as well as angels. Giotto has set apart the religious figures by painting them with halos.

PRIMARY SOURCE: PAINTING

1 **DESCRIBING** Describe the scene shown in the image.

_____

_____

_____

_____

2 **ANALYZING** How are the figures in the painting depicted?

_____

_____

_____

_____

3A **DESCRIBING** Describe the colors used in the painting.

_____

_____

_____

_____

3B **ANALYZING** What mood do these colors create?

_____

_____

_____

_____

4 **INFERRING** Why did Giotto most likely include religious figures and angels in this painting?

_____

_____

_____

_____

ESSENTIAL QUESTION

How do new ideas change the way people live?

Jan Van Eyck's *The Annunciation*

DIRECTIONS: Study the image and answer the accompanying questions.

EXPLORE THE CONTEXT: This Northern Renaissance painting, entitled *The Annunciation*, is a masterpiece created by Jan van Eyck, an artist from the Netherlands. The painting was created around 1434. It depicts an important story from the beliefs of the Roman Catholic Church: The Virgin Mary (on the right) is told by the angel Gabriel (on the left) that she will give birth to the son of God, Jesus.

PRIMARY SOURCE: PAINTING

1 INFERRING How is the scene significant to the Renaissance?

_____

_____

_____

_____

_____

2 DESCRIBING What are some aspects about the painting that stand out to you and why?

_____

_____

_____

_____

_____

3 COMPARING How is this van Eyck painting similar to that of Giotto's _The Lamentation_?

_____

_____

_____

_____

_____

4 COMPARING How is _The Annunciation_ similar to van Eyck's other masterpiece, _The Arnolfini Portrait_ (textbook page 377)?

_____

_____

_____

_____

_____

ESSENTIAL QUESTION

How do new ideas change the way people live?

As you gather evidence to answer the Essential Question, think about:

- the significance of the Scientific Revolution.

- the scientists who changed the way people thought about Earth and the wider universe.

- how new ideas were able to spread throughout Europe.

- how the discoveries during this era are linked to today's ideas and knowledge.

My Notes

_____

_____

_____

_____

_____

_____

The Scientific Revolution

DIRECTIONS: Search for evidence in Chapter 10, Lesson 3 to help you answer the following questions.

1 UNDERSTANDING CHRONOLOGY Complete the graphic organizer below to explain how geographic exploration influenced the development of science.

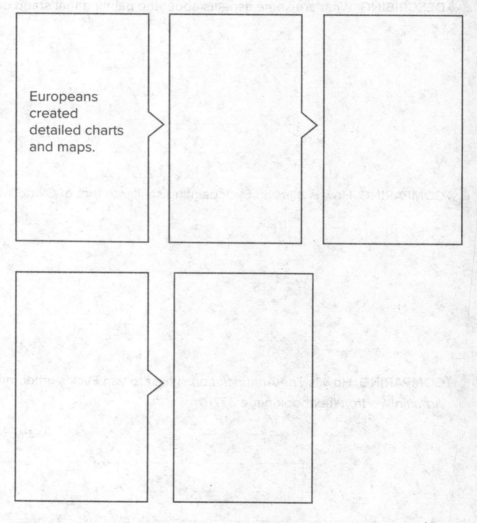

Europeans created detailed charts and maps.

2 EXPLAINING ISSUES What prompted English thinker Francis Bacon to develop the scientific method?

_____

3 **COMPARING** Complete the Venn diagram.

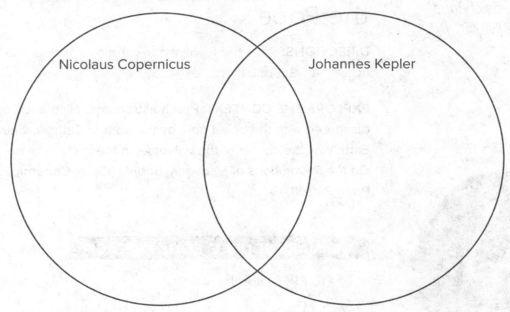

Nicolaus Copernicus   Johannes Kepler

4 **IDENTIFYING EFFECTS** Complete the following chart about Italian scientist Galileo Galilei.

Contribution	Contribution's Purpose or Result
Designed and built his own telescope	
Improved how clocks operated	
Invented a water thermometer	
Conducted experiments with weight and objects	

5 **EXPLAINING** How did dissection affect the Scientific Revolution?

_____

_____

_____

ESSENTIAL QUESTION

How do new ideas change the way people live?

Copernicus's Explanation to the Pope

DIRECTIONS: Read the following excerpt and answer the accompanying questions.

EXPLORE THE CONTEXT: Polish astronomer Nicolaus Copernicus disagreed with the belief held by the Roman Catholic Church that Earth was the center of the universe. In the preface to his book *On the Revolutions of Heavenly Bodies* (1543), Copernicus addresses Pope Paul III.

PRIMARY SOURCE: BOOK PREFACE

"TO POPE PAUL III

I can easily conceive, most Holy Father, that as soon as some people learn that in this book which I have written concerning the revolutions of the heavenly bodies, I ascribe certain motions to the Earth, they will cry out at once that I and my theory should be rejected. For I am not so much in love with my conclusions as not to weigh what others will think about them, and although I know that the meditations of a philosopher are far removed from the judgment of the laity, because his endeavor is to seek out the truth in all things, so far as this is permitted by God to the human reason, I still believe that one must avoid theories altogether foreign to orthodoxy. Accordingly, when I considered in my own mind how absurd a performance it must seem to those who know that the judgment of many centuries has approved the view that the Earth remains fixed as center in the midst of the heavens, if I should, on the contrary, assert that the Earth moves. **"**

— Nicolaus Copernicus, *On the Revolutions of Heavenly Bodies*, 1543

VOCABULARY

conceive: imagine
ascribe: assign
meditations: thoughts
laity: church congregation

foreign: not related to
orthodoxy: custom
assert: declare, defend

1 **SUMMARIZING** What does Copernicus think the reaction of most people will be to his theory?

_____

_____

_____

_____

2 **DETERMINING CONTEXT** What does Copernicus mean when he says his thoughts are "far removed from the judgment of the laity?"

_____

_____

_____

_____

_____

3 **IDENTIFYING PERSPECTIVES** Why is the phrase "so far as this is permitted by God to the human reason" significant?

_____

_____

_____

_____

_____

4 **PREDICTING** How do you think the Roman Catholic Church reacted to Copernicus's book?

_____

_____

_____

_____

_____

ESSENTIAL QUESTION

How do new ideas change the way people live?

VOCABULARY

devout: serious, heartfelt
supplicating: praying, appealing, begging

dost: does
promote: encourage
exulted: rejoice

Kepler's Prayer

DIRECTIONS: Read the following excerpt written by German astronomer Johannes Kepler and answer the accompanying questions.

EXPLORE THE CONTEXT: Using mathematics, Kepler supported Copernicus's theory that the planets revolved around the sun, not Earth. He also proposed other ideas regarding planets and how they moved. Devoted to his work, Kepler's efforts are considered the beginning of modern astronomy.

PRIMARY SOURCE: BOOK

❝ It now remains that at last, with my eyes and hands removed from the tablet of demonstrations and lifted up towards the heavens, I should pray, devout and supplicating, to the Father of lights: O Thou Who dost by the light of nature promote in us the desire for the light of grace, that by its means Thou mayest transport us into the light of glory, I give thanks to Thee, O Lord Creator, Who hast delighted me with Thy makings and in the works of Thy hands have I exulted. Behold! now, I have completed the work of my profession, having employed as much power of mind as Thou didst give to me. . . . ❞

— Johannes Kepler, *Harmonies of the World*, 1619

1 **ANALYZING** Who is Kepler speaking to in this excerpt? What message does he share?

_____

_____

_____

_____

2 **DESCRIBING** Describe the mood of the excerpt.

_____

_____

_____

_____

_____

_____

3 **EXPLAINING** How does Kepler link God and the natural world?

_____

_____

_____

_____

_____

_____

_____

_____

4 **COMPARING** In addition to their theories, what do Kepler and Copernicus have in common? Use the excerpt from Copernicus's _On the Revolutions of Heavenly Bodies_ to help you.

_____

_____

_____

_____

_____

_____

ESSENTIAL QUESTION

How do new ideas change the way people live?

As you gather evidence to answer the Essential Question, think about:

- how great thinkers both agreed and disagreed about ideas.
- how books of the era promoted nontraditional beliefs and change.
- how the Enlightenment helped the lives of serfs.
- how different rulers chose to treat their subjects during the Enlightenment.

My Notes

_____

_____

_____

_____

_____

_____

_____

The Enlightenment

DIRECTIONS: Search for evidence in Chapter 10, Lesson 4 to help you answer the following questions.

1 CIVICS How did the Age of Enlightenment affect ideas of government?

_____

_____

_____

_____

_____

2 IDENTIFYING CAUSES What events caused England to become a constitutional monarchy?

_____

_____

_____

_____

_____

_____

_____

_____

_____

_____

3 EXPLAINING Explain how the monarchy of France's King Louis XIV differed from the constitutional monarchy of England.

_____

_____

4 CONTRASTING Complete the chart.

Individual	Published Work	How It Affected the Enlightenment
Baron Montesquieu		
Denis Diderot		
Mary Wollstonecraft		
Jean-Jacques Rousseau		

5 COMPARING How were Frederick II of Prussia, Maria Theresa of Austria, and Joseph II of Austria similar?

_____

_____

6 IDENTIFYING EFFECTS What was the result of the Russian serf revolt?

_____

_____

_____

_____

ESSENTIAL QUESTION

How do new ideas change the way people live?

Thomas Hobbes on Man's Worth

DIRECTIONS: Read the following excerpt and answer the accompanying questions.

EXPLORE THE CONTEXT: Thomas Hobbes, an English writer, wrote his book *Leviathan* in 1651. Hobbes had strong feelings about human behavior, essentially believing that people had a natural instinct to be selfish and violent toward others. In the excerpt below, he writes about a person's value, or worth.

PRIMARY SOURCE: BOOK

❝The Value, or WORTH of a man, is as of all other things, his Price; that is to say, so much as would be given for the use of his Power: and therefore is not absolute; but a thing dependant on the need and judgement of another. An able conductor of Souldiers, is of great Price in time of War present, or imminent; but in Peace not so. A learned and uncorrupt Judge, is much Worth in time of Peace; but not so much in War. And as in other things, so in men, not the seller, but the buyer determines the Price. For let a man (as most men do,) rate themselves as the highest Value they can; yet their true Value is no more than it is esteemed by others.

The manifestation of the Value we set on one another, is that which is commonly called Honouring, and Dishonouring. To Value a man at a high rate, is to Honour him; at a low rate, is to Dishonour him. But high, and low, in this case, is to be understood by comparison to the rate that each man setteth on himselfe. ❞

— Thomas Hobbes, *Leviathan*

VOCABULARY

absolute: complete
Souldiers: Soldiers
imminent: pending, about to occur
learned: educated
uncorrupt: honest

esteemed: valued, admired
manifestation: expression
setteth: sets

1 **ANALYZING TEXT** Hobbes uses the example of a soldier in discussing what a person is worth. He says that a soldier has a "great Price in time of War . . . but in Peace not so." What is Hobbes saying about how a change in circumstances can change what soldiers are worth?

_____

_____

_____

_____

2 **ANALYZING POINTS OF VIEW** Describe the tone of the excerpt.

_____

_____

_____

_____

3 **INFERRING** How does Hobbes believe that a person's value is determined?

_____

_____

_____

_____

4 **CONTRASTING** Compare this sentence with the one in question 3: "But high, and low, in this case, is to be understood by comparison to the rate that each man setteth on himselfe." According to Hobbes, what role do individuals take regarding their own worth?

_____

_____

_____

_____

John Locke on the Different Types of Laws

ESSENTIAL QUESTION
How do new ideas change the way people live?

DIRECTIONS: Read the following excerpt and answer the accompanying questions.

EXPLORE THE CONTEXT: John Locke wrote his book *Two Treatises of Government* in 1690. In it, he focused on several ideas of the Glorious Revolution.

PRIMARY SOURCE: POLITICAL TREATISE

❝The obligations of the law or nature cease not in society, but only in many cases are drawn closer, and have by human laws known penalties annexted to them, to inforce their observation. Thus the law of nature stands as an eternal rule to all men, legislators as well as others. The rules that they make for other men's actions, must, as well as their own and other men's actions, be conformable to the law of nature, i.e. to the will of God, of which that is a declaration, and the fundamental law of nature being the preservation of mankind, no human sanction can be good, or valid against it.❞

— John Locke, *Two Treatises of Government*

VOCABULARY

annexted: annexed, seized
inforce: enforce, impose
conformable: able to follow or obey
fundamental: basic
sanction: restriction
valid: legal, official

1 IDENTIFYING What law does Locke believe everyone must obey?

_____

_____

_____

_____

_____

2 ANALYZING TEXT What does Locke mean when he says that the rules, or laws, legislators make must be "conformable to the law of nature"?

_____

_____

_____

_____

_____

_____

_____

3 CIVICS How does Locke view the behavior of legislators compared with other individuals in society?

_____

_____

_____

_____

_____

_____

_____

4 EXPLAINING Explain the role Locke believes God plays in society.

_____

_____

_____

_____

_____

_____

_____

_____

ESSENTIAL QUESTION

How do new ideas change the way people live?

❶ Think About It

Review the supporting questions that you developed at the beginning of the chapter. Review the evidence that you gathered in Chapter 10. Were you able to answer each Supporting Question?

If there was not enough evidence to answer your Supporting Questions, what additional evidence do you think you need to consider?

_____

_____

_____

_____

_____

❷ Organize Your Evidence

Use a chart like the one below to organize the evidence you will use to support your position statement.

Central Idea

Supporting Details

③ Write About It

A position statement related to the Essential Question should reflect your conclusion about the evidence. Write a position statement for the ESSENTIAL QUESTION: *How do new ideas change the way people live?*

_____

_____

_____

_____

_____

_____

_____

_____

_____

_____

_____

④ Talk About It

Work in a small group to present your position statement and evidence. Gather feedback from your classmates before you write your final conclusion. You may choose to refine your position statement after you have discussed it with your classmates. Group members should listen to each other's arguments, ask questions, and offer constructive advice about the statement.

⑤ Connect to the Essential Question

On a separate piece of paper, develop an expository essay to answer the ESSENTIAL QUESTION: *How do new ideas change the way people live?*

CITIZENSHIP
TAKING ACTION

MAKING CONNECTIONS The ideas of the Enlightenment have helped shape the world we live in. Many people during the Enlightenment spoke out against unfair treatment by governments and churches, which changed the laws and the ways people were treated. The courage of these people and the changes they helped to create led to a better way of life for many.

DIRECTIONS: Find something you would like to change in your school or community. Write a school newspaper article, an editorial for your local newspaper, a community education pamphlet, or a Web page that supports the change you would like to make. Include why you would like to make this change, as well as ways in which this change could be implemented.

_____

_____

_____

_____

_____

_____

_____

_____

_____

_____

_____

_____

_____

Age of Exploration and Trade

ESSENTIAL QUESTION
Why do civilizations rise and fall?

Think about how this question might relate to early European explorers, trade, and the impact on the cultures these explorers encountered.

COLLABORATE

TALK ABOUT IT

Discuss with a partner what type of information you would need to know to answer this question. For example, one question might be: What factors contributed to the fall of the Taino civilization on the island of Hispaniola?

DIRECTIONS: Now write three additional questions that would help you explain some of the reasons why civilizations rise and fall.

MY RESEARCH QUESTIONS

Supporting Question 1:

_____

_____

Supporting Question 2:

_____

_____

Supporting Question 3:

_____

_____

ESSENTIAL QUESTION

Why do civilizations rise and fall?

As you gather evidence to answer the Essential Question, think about:

- the effect of technology on European overseas exploration.
- the rise of kingdoms in Europe and its impact on overseas exploration.

My Notes

_____

_____

_____

_____

_____

_____

_____

_____

The Age of Exploration

DIRECTIONS: Search for evidence in Chapter 11, Lesson 1 to help you answer the following questions.

1 **ECONOMICS** What economic choices affected the Europeans' decision to explore?

_____

_____

_____

_____

_____

2 **SEQUENCING** Trace the interactions of the European nations, their explorers, and what they discovered. Use the graphic organizer to show the interactions among the three groups. When sent out, what did the explorers find, and what did they do with what they discovered?

Sending Country	Explorers	Discoveries
Spain		
Portugal		
France		

3 **EXPLAINING CAUSE AND EFFECT** What were some factors that caused Europeans to begin exploring? Use the chart to organize your information.

_____
_____
_____
_____
_____
_____
_____
_____
_____

4 **ANALYZING** How did Vasco da Gama landing on India's coast change the world?

_____
_____
_____
_____
_____
_____

Why do civilizations rise and fall?

Magellan's Voyage

DIRECTIONS: Study the excerpt below and answer the accompanying questions.

EXPLORE THE CONTEXT: *Magellan; The First Voyage Round the World,* by George M. Towle, was written as one in a series of history books. The story provides insights into what early explorers encountered in their quest to discover unknown lands and seas.

SECONDARY SOURCE: BOOK EXCERPT

" What made the heat still more unendurable, the supply of fresh water was now almost exhausted; what remained had become so filthy and nauseous that the wanderers could not drink it without shuddering, and it often made them ill. Then Magellan was grief-stricken to be forced to reduce the rations of his brave and suffering comrades. The only food left consisted of course biscuit and these were, as one who was on board says, "reduced to powder, and full of worms." They had been gnawed and defiled by rats, and were scarcely eatable. But even such food was a rich and rare luxury compared to that to which the poor fellows were at last reduced. In no long time not a biscuit, not a crumb remained. Then they were obliged to do the very thing that Magellan had spoken of, when he said he would go forward, "even if they had to eat the leather off the yards." This miserable apology for food was now, indeed, all that was left. The gaunt and famished sailors tore off the ox-hides under the main yard, which had been placed there to protect the rigging from the strain of the yard. The leather was so tough that the hungry teeth could make no impression upon it. They attached pieces of it to strong cords, and let them trail in the sea for four or five days. When they were thus soaked through, the sailors made a poor pretense of cooking the leather. They placed it over the fire, until it was singed, and then ate it greedily. "

—from *Magellan; or The First Voyage Round the World,* 1879

VOCABULARY

unendurable: not able to tolerate
comrades: members of the same group
defiled: ruined, made filthy
obliged: felt the responsibility to do it
gaunt: bony, thin
famished: starving

rigging: the lines and wires that support the masts on sailing vessels
pretense: to act as if something were true; pretending
singed: charred, scorched, blackened

1 **COMPARING AND CONTRASTING** Reread the "Voyage of Magellan" in Lesson 1 and compare the information with this excerpt.

_____

_____

_____

_____

_____

_____

2 **IDENTIFYING PERSPECTIVES** What does this excerpt lead you to believe about Magellan's character?

_____

_____

_____

_____

_____

3 **HISTORY** What does this excerpt illustrate about the perils of sailing in the age of European exploration?

_____

_____

_____

_____

4 **SUMMARIZING** Write a brief summary of this excerpt. Analyze the details supporting the central idea before beginning to summarize.

_____

_____

_____

_____

ESSENTIAL QUESTION
Why do civilizations rise and fall?

Vasco da Gama Reaches India

DIRECTIONS: Study the excerpt below and answer the accompanying questions.

EXPLORE THE CONTEXT: This excerpt is a narrative of the voyages of Vasco da Gama. Some historians believe it is more accurate than other accounts. Gaspar Correa traveled to India only a few years after the land was discovered. Correa found the diary of a priest, Joam Figueira, who reportedly had accompanied da Gama on his voyages. To preserve everything he had learned about the events in India, Correa began writing. This passage has been translated from the Portuguese.

SECONDARY SOURCE: BOOK EXCERPT

" . . . this was a great mountain which is on the coast of India, in the kingdom of Cananor, which the people of the country in their language call the mountain Delielly, and they call it "of the rat," and they call it Mount Dely, because in this mountain there were so many rats that they never could make a village there. . . . and they went on approaching the land until they saw the beach, and they ran along it and passed within sight of a large town of thatched houses inside a bay, which the pilots said was named Cananor, where many skiffs were going about fishing; and several came near to see the ships and were much surprised, and went ashore to relate that these ships had so much rigging and so many sails and white men; which having been told to the King he sent some men of his own to see, but the ships had already gone far, and they did not go. "

—from *The Three Voyages of Vasco da Gama and His Viceroyalty*, 1525

VOCABULARY

Cananor: a monarchy-ruled region in old India

thatched: a roof covering of leaves, straw, etc.

skiffs: small boats to sail or row

rigging: the ropes that attached to sails on the masts and yards

1 **ANALYZING** From this description, how were the explorers greeted when they were first sighted? Explain.

_____

_____

_____

2 **COMPARING AND CONTRASTING** How is the excerpt similar to or different from the lesson text describing Vasco da Gama's discovery? Explain which one helps you understand the human interaction best and why you think so.

_____

_____

_____

_____

3 **ECONOMICS** How would Vasco da Gama's discovery of India's coast have an economic impact on both countries?

_____

_____

_____

_____

4 **INFERRING** In Lesson 1, you read of the early European explorers and their discovery of new lands and cultures. What do you believe were the motivations that caused explorers and monarchies to risk lives and fortunes to accomplish these great explorations? What was often the impact to the cultures found? Explain your views, citing text evidence to support them.

_____

_____

_____

_____

ESSENTIAL QUESTION

Why do civilizations rise and fall?

As you gather evidence to answer the Essential Question, think about:

- Spain's invasions of Cuba and Mexico in search of gold and power.
- the conquest of Peru, allowing Spain to have access to most of South America.

My Notes

_____

_____

_____

_____

_____

_____

_____

_____

_____

_____

Spain's Conquests in the Americas

DIRECTIONS: Search for evidence in Chapter 11, Lesson 2 to help you answer the following questions.

1 **COMPARING AND CONTRASTING** Look closely at the interactions between Cortés and the Aztec rulers and Cortés and some of the Maya people. Use the Venn diagram below to show the similarities and differences.

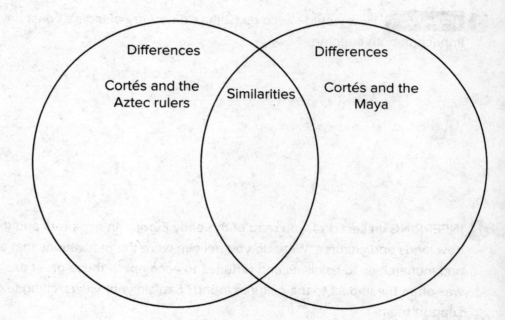

Differences

Cortés and the Aztec rulers

Similarities

Differences

Cortés and the Maya

2 RELATING EVENTS Create a 5Ws map to integrate the information in the lesson about how Spain conquered Peru.

_____
_____
_____
_____
_____
_____
_____
_____

3 ECONOMICS The Spanish monarchs decided to invest in exploration of the America's. What did their investment yield for Spain?

_____
_____
_____
_____
_____
_____

4 SUMMARIZING What is the central idea in Lesson 2? Cite the most relevant supporting details as you explain.

_____
_____
_____
_____
_____

ESSENTIAL QUESTION
Why do civilizations rise and fall?

The Execution of Vasco Núñez de Balboa

DIRECTIONS: Study the excerpt below and answer the accompanying questions.

EXPLORE THE CONTEXT: Vasco Núñez de Balboa is well known as a Spanish explorer, but his life and journeys are not discussed as much as other Spanish explorers. In this excerpt from his biography, Balboa has been charged with treason, imprisoned, and brought out to his execution.

VOCABULARY

naught: nothing
dauntless: fearless
mien: facial expression
yore: days in the past
public crier: someone from the court who announces

usurper: one who uses force to take what is not his
augment: to increase in size
dominions: government territory

SECONDARY SOURCE: BIOGRAPHY

❝But the day had arrived, Balboa's last on earth. The hot afternoon wore away and the sun sank towards the mountains which the prisoner had been the first to explore, and touched with its rays the roofs of the dwellings he himself had erected. The dungeon door was thrown open, and forth came Balboa, preceded by his jailer and loaded with clanking chains. But the burden of the chains was as naught to the armor he had carried in the days of his great deeds, and he bore himself erect, dauntless in mien as of yore. . . . Preceding the prisoner walked the public crier, who announced: "This is the punishment inflicted by command of the king and his lieutenant, Don Pedrarias de Avila, governor of this colony, upon this man, as a traitor, and usurper of lands belonging to the crown." "Nay, nay," exclaimed the still loyal Balboa when he heard this lie proclaimed; "It is false! You, my former comrades, know it is false. Never hath thought of such a crime entered my mind. I have ever served my king with truth and loyalty, and ever sought to augment his dominions!❞

— from *Vasco Núñez de Balboa,* by Frederick A. Ober, 1906

1. **COMPARING AND CONTRASTING** How does the description of Balboa's conviction of wrongdoing in Lesson 2 compare with the excerpt? Does one support the other, and if so, how?

_____

_____

_____

2. **DESCRIBING** Balboa calls the charges against him false. Underline the words that are used to describe Balboa that appear to support his claim of innocence.

_____

_____

_____

_____

3. **CIVICS** What civic virtues, or dedication to the monarchy at his own expense, are found in Balboa's statements?

_____

_____

_____

4. **HISTORY** What were the effects of the charge of treason against Balboa? Cite evidence from Lesson 2.

_____

_____

_____

_____

ESSENTIAL QUESTION

Why do civilizations rise and fall?

A Chronicle of the Spanish Conqueror Cortés

DIRECTIONS: Study the excerpt below and answer the accompanying questions.

EXPLORE THE CONTEXT: The excerpt jumps into a description of the conflict between Spanish explorer Hernán Cortés and the Aztec ruler, Montezuma II. Based on an Aztec legend, a God who opposed human sacrifice said he would someday return. Because of this, Montezuma did not act aggressively toward Cortés when the Spanish landed.

SECONDARY SOURCE: BOOK

❝In the mind of Montezuma, meanwhile, the grave question has been: Can these Spaniards, these strangers of the sunrise, be gods? When Grijalva's expedition appeared off the coast in 1518, it had been reported to Tenochtitlan that in the 'waters of heaven,' as the open sea was called, 'floating towers' had appeared, from which had descended beings with white faces and hands, with beards and long hair, and wearing raiment of brilliant colors and 'round headcoverings.' Could these beings be priests or heralds of the Fair God Quetzalcoatl, come, according to the Maya-Nahua tradition, to resume sway over his people? Before proof could be adduced, Grijalva had departed; and then, shortly, had come swift messengers with news of Cortés and with pictures of his 'floating towers' and of his fair-visaged, yet bearded attendants, handling the thunder and bestriding fierce creatures . . .❞

—from *The Spanish Conquerors, a Chronicle of the Dawn of Empire Overseas*, 1919

VOCABULARY

grave: serious or solemn

Grijalva: another explorer (from Cuba) who visited the coast of Mexico

expedition: journey

raiment: clothing

sway: to have power over something or someone

visage: the appearance or expression of a person's face

bestriding: putting a leg on either side of something, such as a horse

1 HISTORY How is the reaction of Montezuma to the strangers in his land related to another event in recent history for the Aztec? Use details from the excerpt to support your response.

_____

_____

_____

_____

2 COMPARING AND CONTRASTING Examine the description of Montezuma's reaction to Cortés in Lesson 2 and see whether the excerpt corresponds. Describe whether the ideas are in agreement, and support your claim with evidence from the text.

_____

_____

_____

_____

_____

3 ANALYZING What words are used to describe a possible danger to the Aztec? Underline the vocabulary that applies and explain what you think the words represent. Cite evidence of something similar in Lesson 2.

_____

_____

_____

_____

4 DRAWING CONCLUSIONS How does Montezuma's religious belief affect his strategies to defeat the Spanish? Cite evidence from the excerpt and the lesson.

_____

_____

_____

ESSENTIAL QUESTION

Why do civilizations rise and fall?

As you gather evidence to answer the Essential Question, think about:

- the establishment of European empires in the Americas.
- the global exchange of trade known as the Columbian Exchange.

My Notes

_____

_____

_____

_____

_____

_____

_____

_____

_____

_____

Exploration and Worldwide Trade

DIRECTIONS: Search for evidence in Chapter 11, Lesson 3 to help you answer the following questions.

1 **IDENTIFYING** In the 1600s, what areas did Spain, Portugal, France, England, and the Netherlands control in the Americas? In the chart below, identify the areas where each country established settlements.

Country	Areas of Settlements in the Americas
Spain	
Portugal	
France	
England	
The Netherlands	

2 **ECONOMICS** What was the French goal for colonizing North America? Cite text evidence to explain your answer.

_____

_____

_____

_____

_____

_____

_____

3 DESCRIBING What steps did England take to establish North American settlements?

_____

_____

_____

_____

_____

4 EXPLAINING As Europeans established empires in the Americas, world trade changed in many ways. Three results of those changes in world trade were mercantilism, the Commercial Revolution, and the Columbian Exchange. In the chart below, explain what each of those was.

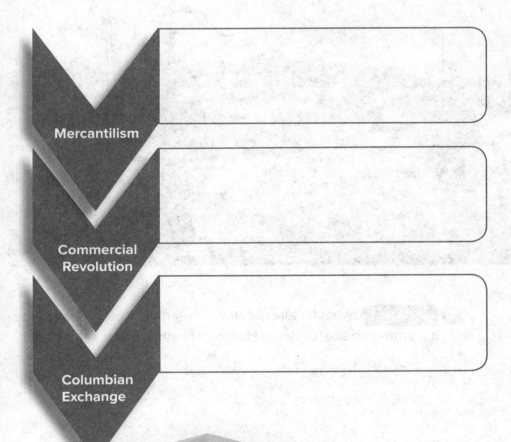

Mercantilism

Commercial Revolution

Columbian Exchange

ESSENTIAL QUESTION

Why do civilizations rise and fall?

New Amsterdam

DIRECTIONS: Examine the image below and answer the accompanying questions.

EXPLORE THE CONTEXT: This image shows a harbor scene in New Amsterdam, now known as New York City, in 1667. The original illustration was created c. 1700s.

PRIMARY SOURCE: ILLUSTRATION

1 **GEOGRAPHY** What features of New Amsterdam's geography made it a promising site for Henry Hudson's North America settlement?

_____

_____

_____

_____

2 **DESCRIBING** Describe the modes of transportation shown. After referring to the text, what can you infer about the larger sailing vessels in the New Amsterdam harbor?

_____

_____

_____

_____

_____

_____

_____

_____

3 **INFERRING** What might the image reveal about the Dutch settlement on Manhattan Island that is _not_ found in the text?

_____

_____

_____

_____

_____

_____

4 **HISTORY** What was happening globally that may have motivated the Dutch to begin overseas explorations? Cite details from the text that support your claim.

_____

_____

_____

_____

_____

_____

_____

ESSENTIAL QUESTION

Why do civilizations rise and fall?

The Fur Trade

DIRECTIONS: Examine the image below and answer the accompanying questions.

EXPLORE THE CONTEXT: The French who explored and settled in North America established trade relationships with many Native American groups. The French were especially interested in trading or trapping for furs to send back to Europe. Deer hide, known as buckskin, was important in this trade. This engraving shows the Native Americans trapping deer. This piece was originally a wood engraving made c. 1600 by Samuel de Champlain, an explorer hired by the French. During his explorations he wrote journals and sketched images of what he saw and found.

PRIMARY SOURCE: ENGRAVING

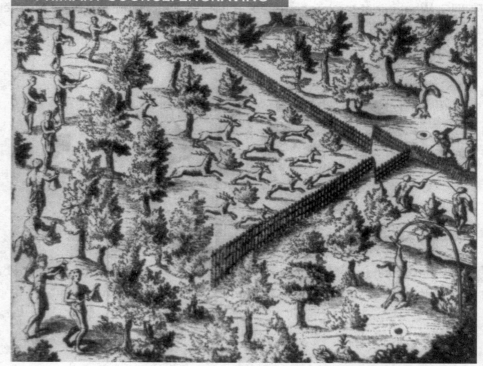

1 **ANALYZING** How are the Iroquois depicted in this image? Describe their actions and what they are doing behind the deer.

_____

_____

_____

2 **DRAWING CONCLUSIONS** Using the visual information in the image, explain why Native Americans might build fencing in the woods.

_____

_____

_____

3 **ECONOMICS** How might the actions of the Iroquois impact them economically?

_____

_____

_____

_____

_____

_____

4 **ANALYZING SOURCES** Using the text from Lesson 3, how might this image relate to European colonies?

_____

_____

_____

_____

_____

ESSENTIAL QUESTION

Why do civilizations rise and fall?

1 Think About It

Review the Supporting Questions that you developed at the beginning of the chapter. Review the evidence that you gathered in Chapter 11. Were you able to answer each Supporting Question?

If there was not enough evidence to answer your Supporting Questions, what additional evidence do you think you need?

_____

_____

_____

_____

2 Organize Your Evidence

Use the chart to organize the evidence you will use to support your position statement. Remember to cite the source of each piece of evidence.

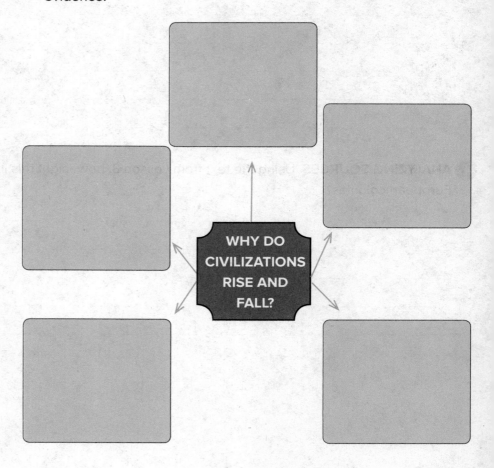

WHY DO CIVILIZATIONS RISE AND FALL?

③ Talk About It

Work with a partner or small group to discuss your position statement and the evidence you have gathered. Before you write your final conclusion, gather ideas from your classmates. Group members should take turns sharing their ideas, asking questions, and offering insights. Use your lesson readings to guide you as you support your ideas.

④ Write About It

Write your position statement for the ESSENTIAL QUESTION, using your gathered information: *Why do civilizations rise and fall?*

_____

_____

_____

⑤ Connect to the Essential Question

With your partner or group, create a slide show presentation about why civilizations rise and fall, using what you've learned in this chapter about civilizations. In developing your presentation, use the evidence you gathered to answer the Supporting Questions. Find images on the Internet to enhance your presentation to make it more visually interesting.

CITIZENSHIP
TAKING ACTION

MAKE CONNECTIONS Think about civilization in North America and in the United States in particular and what you have learned from the text about making a nation strong. List some important elements you feel will keep America thriving.

DIRECTIONS: Choose one element you believe is essential for a nation or civilization to thrive. Then compose a speech that you might deliver to students your age about the future of the United States. In your speech, list the important elements that you think will help America thrive, and emphasize the one element that you think is most important. Use the space here to make an outline of your speech.